Making a living

creating your own job

A self-reliance guide from Backwoods Home Magazine

Contributors —

Gary F. Arnet, Anita Evangelista, Charles A. Sanders, Steven Gregersen, Gary Hutchins, Rosemary LeVernier, Dan Ames, Becky Ames, Dan Shechtman, Mary Kenyon, Emory Warner, Dave Duffy, Nanci Vineyard, Don Wilson, Sharane Wilson, Robert Colby, Dynah Geissal, Jayn Steidl Thibodeau, Rev. J.D. Hooker, J.D. Campbell, Melinda C. Long, Charles O'Sullivan, Jill Fox, John McLane, RN, Cynthia Andal, Sherry Wietelman, Donn Rochlin, Dorothy Ainsworth, Don Fallick, John Silveira

ISBN 978-0-9821577-4-9
Copyright 1991-2009

Backwoods Home Magazine
PO Box 712
Gold Beach, Oregon 97444
www.backwoodshome.com

Edited by Ilene Duffy, Rhoda Denning, and Lisa Nourse
Drawings and cover art by Don Childers

Contents

Introduction

It's been said, "Opportunity only knocks once." The fact is, it pounds on the door constantly. But you now have in your hands a handbook filled with money-making job opportunities. They are drawn from almost 20 years of *Backwoods Home Magazine*. All of these opportunities have proven to be both practical and rewarding for the *BHM* writers themselves or for people they've known firsthand.

Some of our writers, such as Anita Evangelista and Charles Sanders, present a blizzard of opportunities to consider and provide a description of each. Others, like Gary Hutchins in his article about bees, Don and Sharane Wilson's about crayfish farming, and Rev. J.D. Hooker's article on small-scale hog production, go into some of the nuts and bolts of what you need to know and do before you commit yourself.

In these tough economic times we hope you'll find something here that fits you perfectly. But, if not, don't be discouraged. Just seeing how so many others have created money-making opportunities may help you to take stock of your own unique talents and abilities and trigger something that will encourage you to invent your own job—or several jobs. Just remember that income opportunities can come from unexpected sources including hobbies, crafts, and some of your own skills that you haven't thought about in years. When you think about it, most jobs are doing something for others that they can't do, don't have the time to do, or are not inclined to do for themselves. It's your job to figure out what those things are. This book will help you.

Bear in mind as you read these pages that some of the articles were run in the early days of the magazine. Since then, the value of money has changed, so both the costs and rewards of many of the income opportunities listed have changed. Now, answer the door, the opportunities are waiting for you.   — John Silveira

Creating your own job

Creating your own job

By Gary F. Arnet

"I lost my job today," my friend John told me recently. "I have been with the university for five years and with the state budget crisis they just cut my position. I don't know what to do."

As we talked, he said, "You know, I never really liked that job. I was just filling a spot in their bureaucracy and doing it to make a living."

John is not alone. In this tough economy, many in all walks of life are losing their jobs as the national unemployment rate increases. While personal bankruptcies are on the rise, statistics show that 80% of the people who declare bankruptcy could have prevented it if they had only another $500 a month more. Besides those losing their jobs, millions more are bored with what they do every day. Many of those fell into their job because they needed to make money, not because it was their passion.

A job is something you do for a paycheck and quit when the wage stops. A career requires deeper personal investment and marks achievements with money, prestige, or power. A calling, on the other hand, is a passionate commitment to work for its own sake. It is something you love to do and people with callings are happier and more successful than those with jobs or careers.

There are many creative ways to make money and live without a job. That's not to say without working. No, it does take work to make money. It is just that you are not working at a job you don't like.

What made America prosperous and the envy of the world is the American dream of being able to start a business and become

7

successful. To do so, you need the determination to work as hard as it takes to become successful.

So, whether you lose your job, need more money to make ends meet, hate your job, or just want the money to improve your lifestyle, there are ways besides working for someone else that will allow you to do so.

There are endless creative ways to make a living without a job. One of the best ways is to find something you love to do and then figure out how to make money doing it. This may require opening your mind to look beyond what you have done in the past, your current skills, and what others say. Think about what you would really like to do and then figure out a way to get there.

Multiple incomes

Having multiple sources of income is one way to secure financial freedom. Just as it is important to diversify stocks you hold in an investment portfolio, it is important to diversify your income.

You don't want "all your eggs in one basket" when it comes to income. For most people, most of their eggs come from their job, which is at the mercy of their employer and the economy. Lose that and they have lost everything.

Diversify an income by finding multiple sources of income. It is surprising how quick a few dollars adds up. Doing something to earn only $200 a week will create an additional $10,400 a year. Five hundred dollars a week adds up to $26,000. Who couldn't use that?

Let's say that someone loses a job that pays $48,000 a year. It certainly could be hard to find another job at that rate or to start a business that would earn that much. It may be easier to replace that income by finding four smaller sources of $1,000 a month each. They would only need to earn $250 a week from each of these income sources to earn $48,000 a year. Now, that is more achievable.

Sources of income include any ways you can earn money, not just working at a job. Renting out a room in a house, renting storage space in a garage, basement, or for a boat are ways people earn additional income. Some people rent an unused portion of their yard or property to someone who needs space to grow a garden or raise animals. Others rent their house or yard for a movie shoot or for weddings. Buying and renting houses or duplexes can add income.

Small farmers are traditionally masters of making money from every possible source. They have to be if they are going to survive. For example, a family that raises almonds on a small amount of land may not only sell the almond nuts as a crop, they might also sell the almond husks for animal feed, and cut up dead trees to sell as firewood. Most of the nuts might be sold to a distributor, but they may save some to make flavored nuts and almond butter to be sold at farmer's markets and craft fairs.

They might use land around their barn to rent out space for horses, selling the horse manure for compost, and also have a large garden from which they raise herbs, vegetables, and flowers to sell at a farmer's market.

Chickens may be raised to sell their eggs. The chicken manure, along with the horse manure, may be used to raise earthworms for sale, selling the manure as compost afterwards. They might even rent a nice shaded area by a creek for weddings or giving farm tours to "city folks" for a fee. Sure this is a lot of work, but every little bit helps.

Your niche may not be in agriculture, but this example shows how you can find every possible way to make money off your main product or service.

Cut spending

One of the easiest ways to make money is not to spend it. For every $100 a person spends, they need to earn at least $125 to $150 to pay all the payroll, income, and sales taxes. While the last thing most of us want to do is to cut spending, it really can make a huge difference in the amount you need to earn in the first place.

A bankruptcy court recently sent me a notice about someone who owed me money. Attached was a 10-page list of about 150 businesses and individuals to whom this lady was in debt. There were a few major debts for a house and car, but, by far, most of the $100,000 debt owed was for small amounts under $200. She lived an expensive lifestyle, denying herself nothing, while not even trying to live within her means. She could have very easily avoided bankruptcy by just managing her spending.

If it seems that the money always seems to run out before the end of the month, it may be wise to look for ways to cut back on expenses. Large fixed expenses, such as mortgage, auto, and insurance payments are hard to cut back unless you decide to reduce your lifestyle; however, other expenses can be controlled relatively easily.

Analyze every expense as to whether it is an absolute necessity, important but can be delayed, or simply a luxury or convenience, and decide where to make changes. Nothing says you shouldn't include luxury or convenience expenses, but maybe less expensive ones could be used or items purchased less often.

Financial advisor Ray Martin who writes for CBS MarketWatch.com estimates a family of four in the northeast could save over $8,000 a year without much pain or effort if they saved small amounts in a few areas of their life. He gives the following suggestions.

A couple could save $150 a month by dining out once a month instead of weekly. At least another $100 a month per person could be saved by bringing lunch to work or school instead of buying food and beverage. A pack-a-day smoker would be healthier and could save $120 a month by quitting smoking, more if medical costs associated with smoking are considered.

Bank fees add up tremendously. Avoiding ATM transaction fees, annual credit card fees, and credit card interest and late fees can save quite a bit. Paying bills online can save the cost of postage and checks.

Martin estimates most people could save $800 a year by managing bank fees.

Gasoline is an increasing cost for consumers, especially in some states. Since only high-performance cars, such as BMWs or Mercedes, need high-octane gas, using regular will provide savings. Avoiding unnecessary driving and consolidating errands into one trip can also save on gas costs.

Using energy efficient appliances, lowering the thermostat in the winter and raising it in the summer, insulating water heaters, turning off lights, and other energy saving ideas can save utility costs at least $500 a year or more.

Consumer technology is great, but expensive. Cell phone, additional phone lines, pagers, phone services such as call-waiting, call-forwarding, and answering services, cable or satellite TV subscription service, DSL service, and web service subscriptions can add up to $100 to $200 per month. Decreasing or eliminating unnecessary or minimally used services can add up to large savings.

Consumers can save a considerable amount by buying food in bulk at discount warehouse stores. Individually prepared meals, such as frozen dinners, are expensive. Sodas, chips, cookies, and other "junk foods" are fine on occasion, but limiting them to occasional instead of daily use can improve the diet while saving money. Having a plan for meals and bringing a shopping list to the market limits impulse buying and, therefore, cost.

Evaluate insurance to see if raising deductibles or changing companies can lower costs. Buying auto and homeowner's insurance through the same company can reduce insurance costs by 10 to 15 percent.

There are many other "little" things that don't seem to cost much, but taken together add up. A few hundred here and there and soon you are saving thousands of dollars a year without much sacrifice.

Creating income

When I was talking to John about his job loss, we kept discussing friends we knew who make a living without a job. That is when it struck me how many people do this and what opportunities exist.

While there are hundreds, if not thousands, of ways to make an income doing something you enjoy, sometimes you need to look "outside the box." Instead of looking at established job descriptions, look at what you love to do and then figure out a way to make money at it. Be creative.

Like history? Start a tour business showing people the local historical sites in your town. Like to fish? Become a fishing guide. Like to bake? Make custom-ordered cakes. Like shopping? Become a personal shopper. Like the Internet? Make a commission selling things for others over eBay or other auctions.

Your income can even vary by the season. One friend I know makes a living for his family as a ski instructor and by owning a snow removal company in the winter, while being a water ski instructor and handyman in the summer.

While there are many sources of income out there, most fall into a few broad categories. The stories of the following people are all real, although I have changed their names to protect their privacy.

Service industry

When David left the Army Special Forces he found there was not much of a civilian job market for snipers. Having no other training, he fell into something others don't want to do—washing windows. He has developed a large clientele of businesses and homeowners that allow him to make a good living, while giving him the freedom to travel and go hunting when he wants. This has been his sole source of income for more than 12 years.

His secret? He discovered that many people don't have the time or interest to do routine work around the house and are more than willing

12

to pay to have it done. In fact, it can be hard to find reliable, trustworthy people to do work around your house. Dave does a good job at a fair price and is not afraid of doing other work. Need your gutters cleaned out? Sure, he'll do that. Need a plant moved? Some debris hauled? He'll do that also.

Jan has made a living for 15 years cleaning people's homes. She works full-time and accepts only clients that she likes. She is reliable, thorough, and has a waiting list of people who want her to clean their houses. It is surprisingly hard to find quality and trustworthy cleaners. How did she start? Word-of-mouth. Her first client told their friends about Jan and word spread fast until she was so busy she had to turn business away.

People will pay others to clean their house, clean gutters, rake leaves, shovel snow, do shopping, wash and detail cars, organize closets or garages, take care of their animals, house-sit when they are gone, mow their lawn, clean their pool, manage their flower gardens, and even scoop up dog droppings from their yards. Many people have more money than they have time, making a perfect opportunity for someone looking for work.

Hobbies and crafts

After retiring from a career as a cardiovascular nurse, Ben was looking for a way to spend his time. He took up woodworking on a lathe, making beautiful bowl and lamps from wood he finds near his mountain home. Finding he loved lathe work, he soon had given away bowls to all his friends and still had a garage full of finished products.

He started traveling around to craft and art fairs to sell his extra work. He found in some urban areas he could sell a bowl for several hundred dollars, and, all of a sudden, he was earning several thousand dollars a weekend.

Lisa is 16 years old and makes gorgeous fused glass and silver jewelry. She sells about $1,800 of jewelry a month at art fairs, stained glass stores, and through her website. Not a bad high school income for doing something she loves to do.

Don, a dentist, carves custom gunstocks out of black walnut as a hobby. His work is very elaborate, detailed, and in demand. He works only when he feels like it and customers gladly wait and pay any price since his work is unparalleled.

Homemade crafts of all types are in demand when you find the right market. Judy, a receptionist at an office by day, makes cute, elaborate cookie dough Christmas ornaments while watching television at night. She can sell $1,000 worth of ornaments in a weekend at a craft fair. Not a bad income from a part-time hobby.

Hobby and craft products are certainly a way many people make some extra income while having fun. Some even make a full-time living. Those interested in more information should read *Handmade for Profit: Hundreds of Secrets To Success in Selling Arts and Crafts* by Barbara Barbec.

Teaching a skill

Local community colleges and adult education programs have community education classes that teach everything from bicycle repair, wilderness survival, traveling on a budget, gardening, tamale making, and genealogy to getting out of debt, planning your retirement, and computers.

Classes are taught by instructors who know their topic and not by professional teachers. Most instructors teach because they love their topic and want to pass along their knowledge. Some teach to meet people interested in their field or hobby and others teach to attract future customers in their regular business or to sell books they have written. Instructors are paid to teach the course by the college, making it another small income source.

Parents gladly pay to find qualified teachers in music and art. Tutors are in demand to help students learn mathematics, reading, and science. People pay to learn woodworking, ceramics, stained glass, and other hobbies. Surprisingly, there is even a business in teaching ballroom dancing to couples needing to learn to dance for their wedding. There is demand for just about anything you can teach.

Farming and gardening

Maisie Jane Bertagna was in high school when she started preparing and selling seasoned almonds as a FFA project at school. Her product was a hit and she started Maisie Jane's California Sunshine Products. Now in her 20s, Maisie now employs a number of people and her products are distributed in stores nationwide.

Matt is an almond farmer, but has raised and sold fresh fruits and vegetables at a local farmers market since he was 10 years old. He enjoys spending Saturdays seeing old friends at the market while he supplements his income. Others with small gardens grow specialty vegetables in their yards for sale to local restaurants and organic food stores. There are many ways to make money from your love of growing or raising foods.

Love flowers? How about selling potted or cut flowers? One person set up a business where she grows flowers and has contracted with small businesses to provide them with an arrangement of fresh flowers for their reception room or office every week. Specialty nurseries can be set up on as little as 1000 square feet of land.

Dog breeding can be a profitable and fun way to make some extra money, as can raising other animals. There is a market for almost anything you can raise.

Internet

The Internet is a $900 billion industry that has truly revolutionized the way an individual can do business. Anyone can launch a website and open an online store to sell almost any product or service, reaching a worldwide market that was once only available to large corporations.

Some of the opportunities available include websites to sell products, selling over eBay and other auctions, self-publishing, starting E-zines (electronic magazines), and writing online newsletters on topics that interest you.

Considerable other work is also being done over the Internet. For example, a draftsman I know works from his house receiving jobs from companies over the Internet. He does the work in his free time at night and weekends and returns it via the Internet. Work is so good he is thinking of making this his full-time job.

One nice thing about many Internet businesses is that they do not require you to be available by the phone at all times. Your Internet business is still working while you are at work, play, or even sleeping.

A number of books are available on making income on the Internet, including *Multiple Streams of Internet Income* by Robert Allen.

So much more

Opportunities to earn money are limited only by one's imagination. If you love to travel, why not make money at the same time. Travel income sources include freelance writing for travel magazines, being a photographer, leading group tours, and buying or selling for an import/export business. If you want to travel abroad and know a foreign language you are in even more demand.

People earn money with freelance photography, videotaping weddings, baking, decorating cakes, leading local historical tours, researching family histories, and cutting and selling firewood. Other home businesses include mail order businesses and information products such as audiotapes, videotapes, or computer software. Those with a passion for writing earn money self-publishing books, writing for magazines, and creating newsletters.

The possibilities are literally unlimited. Finding your passion is the first step in making an income without a job. If you follow your love, the money will follow. For other ideas read *Careers for Non-Conformists* by Sandra Gurvis or *Making a Living Without a Job* by Barbara J. Winter.

16

You can keep trudging along complaining about your life and waiting for something to magically change or you can do something about it. Find your calling and take the steps to follow your dreams. Whether you are trying to earn some extra income or looking for a new career, the possibilities are endless. 🙠

10 ways to make money on your land

By Anita Evangelista

There's something very visceral about having your own piece of land, whether it's a little scrap of green terrace or a vast expanse of fertile bottomland. Ownership (or rentership) of ground tugs at a series of primal instincts—to cultivate, to promote growth, to improve, and ultimately to enjoy the rewards of your efforts. Urban dwellers satisfy this drive by planting flowers in window boxes and herbs in pots on apartment ledges. Suburbanites lavish attention and money on carpet-thick lawns and sculpted terraces. Rural denizens concentrate their efforts on a particular field or specific livestock. Yet, in each case, there is always an ultimate goal, to manage the soil and land to achieve some direct benefit.

Now, this is a good thing. The discovery that good land management returns a financial and emotional reward tends to promote better management in the future, which is also a good thing! The challenge, of course, is figuring out the thing that will bring the best return, using the abilities and skills you already have, and fitting your efforts into the time you have available. Sometimes, that combination of parameters creates a daunting barrier to further action: I've only got a backyard lawn, and a little time on weekends; how can I possibly earn any income off of that?

To answer that, I can share my experience. When we lived in Los Angeles in a miniscule city home, our entire lot was 40 feet wide and

70 feet long. (Later, when we lived on a farm, our garden was bigger than that!) In that space, a small house, garage, concrete patio, and grassy yard all seemed too tiny to squeeze in anything that might have contributed to making an additional income, but somehow, we managed. We grew grapes up a chicken-wire lattice on the south side of the house, and planted highly productive dwarf fruit trees and harvested dozens of pounds of peaches, apples, and apricots every year. Not only was the flavor better than store-bought, by growing our own we avoiding having to spend money on fruit. We created a tiered 4'x4' strawberry "patch" that provided luscious berries all year around. Our front chain link fence provided a trellis for chayote vines, which routinely gave over 100 pounds of "squash" yearly.

At one point, we housed over 60 breeding rabbits, stacked like apartment dwellers in homemade cages three "stories" high. Those bunnies racked up around $7200 net annually, sold to pet shops and private individuals—plus provided a significant protein complement to our diet and some of the finest fertilizer available for our garden and our friends' gardens as well. A tall, narrow, multi-level cage housed over 100 Coturnix quail, fast reproducing and mini-egg laying wonders. We sold eggs and chicks, plus had all the "gourmet" eggs we could eat. The concrete patio provided an area for hubby Nick to teach fencing (the sword kind), and an old upright piano in the small living room provided a place for me to give piano lessons. And, of course, both Nick and I wrote and sold freelance non-fiction articles by sharing time on an IBM Selectric typewriter. We both were at home all day, so our children were homeschooled, too. Remember, this was on a lot smaller than a country garden. If we could do it, so can you!

A personalized plan

Earning a profit from your land, honestly, won't be instantaneous and will require effort. As a quick refresher, consider this: there are only three main things that you can sell. I'm going to emphasize these, because any one or combination of these can be the basis for your own

19

plan-for-profit off your land:

• Products: items you make, build, improve, develop, grow, or produce to provide a good that buyers need or want.

• Skills: what you can do, teach, explain, or accomplish that provides knowledge or new abilities that people need or want.

You can teach fencing on a small, concrete patio.

• Services: actions you can carry out to serve the needs or wants of other people. Some services are simple manual tasks that potential buyers just don't want to do or can't do on their own (say, cleaning windows or carpets, or locating a special part for an old sewing machine). Others require more complex skills, combining skill and service in one swoop (such as: auto repair, computer debugging, or designing a landscape).

Every step in the process of building your profit system can also be rewarding and satisfying in its own way. Keep in mind that each of the following planning steps takes you closer and closer to your goal.

1. Know your land. This is both simpler and more complex than it sounds. I suggest you draw a map of your available ground, even if it's only a small patio space next to a condo. Get some graph paper or a piece of poster board. Spend several days to a week or so examining and measuring out your available space and draw out your property outlines. Include buildings, concrete areas, trees, reserved areas (kid's play zone, for example), as it currently exists. Remember to look up as well as down; notice building heights, trellises and overhangs, and where sunlight falls. This will be your basic tool for the rest of your progress, so make this detailed enough that you can close your eyes and

visualize the layout readily. Imagine where you could tuck in small cages, planters, or tools.

2. Write out your skills. Again, simpler and more complex than it appears. Those abilities you take for granted (say, changing the oil on your car, playing clarinet, training dogs, identifying garden herbs, baking bread from scratch, typing 70 words per minute, and so forth) are NOT free goods. Each skill took you time and effort to acquire, and your time and existing skills all have value. Part of earning money on your land includes accepting the reality that you are allowed to profit from what you know. Don't stop listing your skills until you have at least 15 on your list. Most people can list over 40 skills if they think about it for a while. It helps, also, to consider how much you'd have to pay someone else to do the particular action, too. It might seem easy to replace your house's plastic water pipes, but if you had to hire a plumber to do the same work you'd realize how valuable that skill is.

3. Write down specific benefits of your area. This step can be the trigger to developing your plan, observing and acknowledging those features of your region that promote business development. Take a walk around the area or the neighborhood, notice what kind of businesses already flourish there. Observe the income level (up-scale, moderate, downscale), and what people seem to want. If you supply something people want, you'll be able to sell whatever you produce. Don't try to duplicate existing businesses—create something better, cheaper, or easier to acquire. Keep in mind that some elements that might be uncomfortable in other settings, such as high population density, can be a plus: more potential customers are available.

4. Write down specific limitations of your area. Weather is often a limiting factor in developing income plans—you can't grow fruit outdoors in a Maine winter, for example. If you live an hour's drive from the nearest town, that will limit access from potential buyers. If you live in a gated community, it will be challenging for potential buyers to meet

you spontaneously. This step helps you keep a realistic attitude about your plans.

5. Write down how you want to live in one year, two years, five years. Our goal was to work at home, to make the land we lived on a place of profit as well as a place to sleep—truly, a "homestead." We wanted to raise our children in a safe environment and produce the majority of our own food. Our plan was to acquire a two story house, paid off, in a rural setting that was both productive and pretty—and that's where we landed only four short years after we began working toward that goal. We were not interested in having a huge income, or in amassing IRAs, but you might be. Remember to factor your real (as opposed to desired) income needs in when you set up your plans.

You'll spend a good week or longer sorting out these five steps, but this information will be the foundation for the money-making ideas in the next section.

10 ways to make $$$

The following are meant as introductory concepts, designed to get you thinking. Let each act as a brainstorm-starter—hold an idea in mind, and imagine its ramifications in your setting, on your land. Be sure to write down key points; keep a notebook handy. Don't let a good idea get away because you forgot to write it down.

1. Teach: This can be done in city or country. Look back at your list of skills. What can you do? Play a musical instrument? Ride a horse well? Sing? Dance? Gourmet cooking? Tai chi? Make pottery? Wildcraft herbs? Weave or spin wool? Build a masonry wall? Paint? Karate? Do reflexology massage? Someone in your area wants to learn what you know. In order to teach, you need students. In order to get students, you must advertise locally: word of mouth, posters at local colleges and markets, sharp-looking business cards (make them on your computer), and perhaps a magnetic sign on the doors of your vehicle if your transportation is neat and clean. Put your ads where people likely to want your knowledge might go, such as health food stores, veterinary supply houses, or bookstores. Offer a 500-word how-to article about your area of expertise ("How to grow a great tomato," "How to find a deal on a used car") to your hometown newspaper. Local newspapers often carry short informative pieces by local folk. People will consider you an expert after they see it.

Don't spend much for your initial advertising—start small and let the business begin to pay its own way. Check out the prices of your competition, and underprice them just a little for your first experiences—later, as your client base increases, you can raise your price to middle range or higher. Decide in advance what a "course" will be; 4 weekly meetings for beginners? A 3-hour group meeting on one Saturday morning? Provide a clear, written description of what you teach and what the student can expect from a course. Anticipate what equipment you and your students will require; extra tools for beginners, clean-up supplies, blackboards or computer access. Keep notes on what you did and if it worked, and change how or what you teach to accommodate what you learn about students. Teach the course you wish you had been able to take. Remember, you'll lose a percentage of students—it's not what they expected, too much work, they find another interest—don't take it personally. Give them more than they expect, and keep learning.

2. Raise small stock: We kept rabbits in the city and made a profit. What do people buy in your area? Is it an animal you'd like to raise? How about parakeets, finches, or cockatiels—small space requirements with potential sales to pet shops? Rats are interesting pets, smart, and breed rapidly. Exotic colors or hairless rats, which reproduce just as well as white ones, sell for higher rates. Guinea pigs and hamsters remain popular (though low-profit) pets. Dogs and cats are perennial sellers. Keeping a pair of cats or small dogs in a city or country residence requires no more effort than keeping a single one. They can produce 1-2 litters per year, of 4-6 offspring each time. Aim to produce healthy animals in desired breeds and colors. Smaller dogs cost less to feed than big ones, and sell more readily. Read extensively about dog or cat breeding. If you haven't kept un-neutered animals before—they behave differently than fixed ones, and breeding may require specialized skills or equipment.

Acquire good quality registered breeding stock, from unrelated healthy lines. Avoid "show winners" since they are bred more for looks than for health or personality. Watch out for fad animals, though—iguanas, hedgehogs, pot-bellied pigs, emus, monkeys—they go through phases of public interest and price fluctuations that make Wall Street look tame. Remember, if you consider breeding small stock, that there will be veterinary costs, vaccinations, registration costs, feed requirements, and cages—plus cleaning, handling, walking, and daily care. Healthy, clean, vibrant animals command the highest prices, too. If you like the small stock you raise, it won't be a chore. I would caution you not to sell to pet brokers, however, both because you can't control how your infants are handled by the broker, and because your profit will be much smaller than selling directly to the new owners. Check out the "pets for sale" in your local newspaper for an idea of the profit potential, and what people are buying locally.

3. Hospitality/retreat: If you have several acres of land and an attractive rural location (no matter how far out), consider offering a retreat or holiday getaway spot. Typically, customers for this service are upscale or middle-upper folk, who just want to get away from their usual life into a facsimile of country or wilderness living for a time. "Facsimile" is the key word here. Most often, these clients don't want the discomforts of rural living—flies, odors, power outages, or exposure to real weather. They want to see cows and horses, perhaps pet a goat, and hold an egg minutes after it came from the chicken. They will require phone, electric, internet (wi-fi), air-conditioning, and thermostat-controlled winter heating. This customer base will pay a premium for the country experience, and $750 to $1500 per week is not unrealistic. Keep in mind that these will be high-input clients, who expect to have their whims catered to. The return may make it worthwhile for you.

Alternatively, consider appealing to the back-to-nature person, who just wants a little rough cabin on a hillside, a clean-burning oil lamp, and silence (with daily organic food deliveries to their door, of course). This individual or family may be seeking long country walks, contemplation, and inner renewal, and is generally low-input and largely self-sustaining. Rates of $300 to $500 per week would be reasonable. If you consider this option, write a very clear brochure that details all services offered, and all services NOT offered that someone might expect. Figure liability insurance into your start-up costs, and how you might respond if guests trashed your facility or accidentally set fires.

An interesting bed-and-breakfast in my region is located in a rehabilitated "mansion," located in the middle of the city on its own stream-crossed and tree-shrouded acre. The way the grounds are laid out, guests often think they are deep in the country, and city-noises rarely filter into the rooms. A "selling feature" of the place is that there are NO telephones, TV, videos, smoking, or alcohol in the rooms—this might be considered a liability elsewhere. However, in this facility, peace and quiet are the main selling points. Rooms run $100 to $180 per night ($700 to $1260 weekly) and the place is almost always full. Advertise online to reach the largest audience ("yourname.com" websites run about $20 per month through Yahoo and other companies), and search "vacation retreats" to see the vast potential in this option.

4. Middleman: If you enjoy exploring country auctions and have a good eye for local costs versus prices for the same items in larger metro areas, you might be a natural middleman (middleperson?). When we were raising sheep, a clean shorn fleece from heirloom breeds of sheep (Cotswold, Jacobs, Lincolns, for example) were hard to sell in the country—they were too different from the plain white commercial wools that wholesalers wanted. Jacob fleece, with its white, brown, and black colors, was discounted by buyers to as low as 23 cents per pound. But, in the city, a single pound of the same Jacob wool sold for $8 to $10 at specialty shops! A middleman who was willing to pick up, say,

100 pounds of Jacob wool and pay a fair $1 per pound to the shepherd, could drive that wool a couple hundred miles and turn that $100 investment into $400-$500 (half what the retail store charges).

The secret is knowing where to find the product and where to sell it. Begin by checking out products for which you already have an interest—antiques? Oil paintings? Quilts? Old farm tools? Classic cars? Compare local prices in the newspaper with prices in various "big city" papers. You might also check eBay or other online marketplaces for "national" rates. I know a couple who sold a doll collection for a relative at a local auction. The dozens of dolls included some dolls that dated back to the Revolutionary War. The collection brought around $300, and the couple received 10% for their efforts. They thought they did pretty well, until they found that one single doll from that collection was valued at over $2000. Imagine if they had taken the time and gone through the trouble to put the whole collection, one by one, on eBay or other auctions. Would their time as middlemen have been well-spent? Remember, too, that you can middleman single items. One time, we found a Japanese antique figurine at a thrift store. Bought it immediately for an "outrageous" (for that shop) $14, walked it across the street to an antique shop and resold it for $125. A week later, we saw it featured in the shop's front window for $300! I've often wondered if the original owner, who gave it away to the junk store, ever saw it and realized his or her mistake.

5. Mobile services: If you have a skill and equipment, there's no law that says potential buyers have to come to you—you can go to them, instead. I've seen "computer repair on-call" vans, mobile "meat processors," and "car repair clinics" on wheels. Each service is carried on from a home base that consists of equipment, a vehicle, and a cell phone, plus the owner's skill, of course. Locally, we even have a genuine doctor whose "office" is his car—he makes house calls to hotels and student dorms. Payment rates include the service provider's hourly rate plus a little extra for the house-call expense, and are generally made by check or cash. Higher-priced services might offer an estimate for a small fee (to cover the house call itself). Potential customers are rural residents who don't want to transport their steer, computer, or broken whatzit to appropriate facilities, and are happy to pay an additional charge for the convenience of having the service come to them. The "convenience" aspect is an excellent selling point—save valuable time and personal energy, and avoid the difficulty of taking your item in for service. Each service is different, but if appearances are any indicator, their vehicles act as a primary means of advertisement: name, type of service, and contact phone number are on the vehicle's sides and back.

6. Specialty services to a niche market: A niche business is one that appeals to a small group or special interest, that is, a marketing niche (pronounced nitch). For hunters, there are niche "backcountry guides" who will take a small group out to the back 80 acres during quail or deer season—for a fee, of course. In the same way, setting up a portion of your land for specialty events or hobbies may be the way to go. How about a special place for black powder fans or bow hunters to shoot at various types of targets? Or a meeting place for stock dog trainers to try out their dogs (need sheep for this, naturally). Would an indoor shooting range work on your property? Or, perhaps, an outdoor training facility of any kind?

You can raise small stock to sell to individuals or markets.

Niche marketing can also include raising meat "by subscription," that is, arranging in advance who will buy your rabbits, goats, lambs, chickens, turkeys, geese, sides of beef or pork, or even some exotic birds like quail or pheasant. Advertise by brochure at farmer's markets and health food stores, provide incredibly healthy animals and tasty meat, and hand out recipes to potential customers. After we left the farm, we continued to acquire lamb by subscription. In the spring we agreed to buy two grown-out lambs in August from a small backyard flock. We put a small deposit on each lamb ($25 per head), and agreed that we would pay market price less the deposit when they were ready. Come the fall, lambs were ready for market but we were busy, so the seller was happy to haul them to the processor for an extra $25. We also paid for the processing costs so the seller received above market price for a virtually guaranteed sale, and had some start up funds to help pay for feed costs. The deposit was non-refundable, by the way. The same could be done with an assortment of vegetables, too, if your gardening efforts tend to be super-abundant. Give buyers a choice of three different plans (exotic veggies, table veggies, cooking veggies, for example), and have them pay half up front.

7. Landscaping plants: This is a bit closer to farming, but can actually be done on a very small amount of space, including a well-planned suburban backyard. The goal is not to compete with nearby businesses that sell trees and the usual assortment of foundation plantings, but to sell yourself as somehow exotic, extra fancy, or "more natural" than other businesses. For instance, you could offer "edible landscaping" only—plants that provide food in some form, as well as look attractive. This might be a little higher priced than conventional landscaping, too. If you've already got a green thumb and some gardening sense, this could be a good parttime option, as well. Start up costs would include seeds or plant starts, potting soil, and containers. Check out websites for bulk purchases of your basic supplies or exotics you can grow. Consider setting up a "hoop house" made from PVC pipe and a piece of construction plastic as a moveable greenhouse. Keep in mind that this is very seasonal income, and remember to provide information specific to the items you are selling (how to prepare those "sand cherries" or fry day lily buds, for example).

8. Touring: Every region has its attractions. Out-of-towners who like to see what is off the beaten path may be seeking a small regional touring service, especially if it offers something special—say, a day tour of

28

Amish country in a horse-drawn buggy? If you have that horse and wagon set up already, you may be halfway to accomplishing this business. Alternatively, a sturdy clean van might do (you'll need a chauffeur's license, too). The other half of starting up is knowing some interesting information about your area, preparing a tour program or set of stops, and, of course, advertising it. Local hotels and motels, gas stations, and tourist restaurants may allow you to put up flyers or set out brochures (which can be made on your home computer). Describe the tour, include some photographs of your ride, and have a few stops where passengers can get out and pick an ear of corn or shop at a roadside stand. Be prepared with a list of recommendations for realtors, restaurants, and good auto mechanics in case riders ask.

9. Pond fishing and casting pools: Even in the heart of the Ozarks, where nearly every stream and lake is saturated with catfish, an older gent runs a pond fishery that specializes in catfish. Basically, he's got a few spring-fed ponds into which he puts catfish fingerlings every year or so. He tosses in some catfish food when he remembers. When customers come by, he offers a fishing pole rental, a container of bait (the customer is now $7 into this), and all the time the customer wishes to spend sitting under a shady tree holding that rented pole over a pond. When the customer catches a fish, the gent will weigh it (and charges 49 cents a pound for this fish), and then cleans it for an extra $2 if you want, thereby shaving off about $1/3$ the "value" to toss back into the pond to feed the other fish. Anyway, that one catfish will end up costing about $12—not too bad a markup for a $1 fish! He could make a little more if he offered soda pop, cold sandwiches, chips in small bags, or other pre-packaged snacks, as well. How about adding a picnic table so the missus could rent a portable BBQ or camp stove (extra $5 or so) and cook that fish right there? This operation would be seasonal, and would have some interesting potentials for expansion (offering "fishing vacation" campsites or even training camps for using certain kinds of rods/reels or bait).

10. Petting zoo, historical farm: If you like small animals, the petting zoo or historical "re-creation" farm might be your ideal. A petting zoo is nothing more elaborate than a collection of tame, docile, friendly animals located where people can touch them. Sadly, in our culture, the average person has very little interaction with live animals. This idea is a natural attraction for children and animal-loving adults. Basically, the animals would need to be kept in a small enclosure or yard where they could move around with some freedom. Patrons arrive at the gate (have parking available), pay their fee (say, $3 each), and enter the enclosure. Here they see the small angora goat, a pair of rabbits, a potbellied pig, several chickens and ducks, and perhaps an emu or some other unusual animal. At a rack near the front gate, you've got a bag of whole feed corn and a set of inexpensive edible ice cream cones. For only $1.50, children can fill their cones with corn, and feed the animals (thereby saving you a daily chore and paying for it at the same time)! You may be able to contact local schools and offer school specials: children on the field trip bus enter for only $1 each, plus you can give a little chat about the attributes of each animal ("chickens lay eggs"). You don't have to inform anybody that everything except the emu is going to end up on your dinner table in the fall. Be sure to form an alliance with a local veterinarian to keep vaccinations and other care up to date, and keep the visible facility spotlessly clean—people sometimes misunderstand the realities of animal care.

Historical farms take a different route. If you have an interest in old-time skills (blacksmithing, weaving, spinning, leather working, etc.), you can set up a small backyard operation that capitalizes on your abilities. Dress in period clothes, surround yourself with period goods such as candles or oil lamps, and be willing to give a demonstration of your talents. You may be able to focus your demonstration days on one or two days a week (say, Fridays and Saturdays), and include colleagues who have their own skills. Somebody here in the Ozarks did set up an arrangement like this with a few craftspeople and some hillbilly décor —they called it Silver Dollar City. It's doing pretty well, last I heard.

Finally...

Let these ideas be a starting point for your own potential business. Brainstorm, read, check the internet, and figure out your costs versus the probable returns. Assume your new business will probably not pay for itself the first year, and may just break even the second year. After that, growth! If you keep at it, the possibility of living comfortably right off your land grows, too. ✒

35 country jobs

By Charles A. Sanders

$\mathcal{I}$f you're relocating to the backwoods, you will very likely have to give some thought to generating some income, that is, making a living. Hopefully, the topic is one you've prepared for prior to making the jump, getting the cart and horse in the proper order, you know.

Most of us desire a lifestyle for ourselves and our families which a small homestead can simply not support. There are outside expenses that frequently present themselves and even the most self-sufficient homesteader requires some items which cannot be produced on the place. To be able to buy, build, maintain, and keep our place in the country, most of us are required to seek outside "gainful employment." If you fall into that category, don't get discouraged. Simply make the most of where you are. It is no crime to work away from home to be able to keep your place in the country.

Living in the backwoods is the dream of countless people. But not only do you still need a way to support yourself and your family, you will find that in remote and rural areas jobs are often harder to come by and they usually pay less.

Our local community is based around a county seat of fewer than 900 people. The entire county has around 10,000 residents. Accordingly, most of the folks who enter the job market—there are plenty who don't bother—are required to venture into the neighboring counties and larger population centers, work at one of the relatively few jobs available nearby, or work at their own businesses.

Some of the people described in this article have more than one pursuit that contributes to their income. Some couples pursue their work independently, others team up. Some have expanded upon something they already enjoy doing, while others have recognized the need for a product or service and used that to form the basis of a supplemental income. Basically, they created their own "second job."

These are the friends and neighbors among whom I live, here in my southern Indiana county. Despite the diversity in job interests, all share a common bond: the desire to live in our small rural county. Perhaps their ingenuity in finding a source of income for themselves will spark your own imagination in doing the same.

Crafts

Patti, my wife, has made good money by making and selling Santas and other figures, dried wreaths, swags, and other crafts. She has a real eye for color and design, so these crafts come rather naturally for her. We have traveled to a couple of craft shows and have had the items set up in a "mini-mall" booth. Wholesaling to independent vendors has also been somewhat successful. If you decide to sell to retail shops and stores, plan to visit them during the off-season, because that's when retail stores buy original craft items. Patti has also found that word of mouth sales have been productive.

Sheep, hogs, steer

Patti's Santas require the use of long, soft wool for the making of their beards and hair. For that, we visit a friend who runs her small business in the adjacent county. She makes money from her herd of Cotswold sheep by selling wool to spinners and other

Raising hogs or beef steers for custom sale can be profitable.

33

craftspeople. She cleans and combs the wool herself and charges by the pound for the finished material. By selling to local craftspeople, she is able to charge a higher (read fairer) price than for raw wool.

Particularly in areas with a large multicultural population, lamb is a very popular meat and raising lambs for slaughter can make you some good money. You can easily get a good price for your lambs with a simple advertisement in the local paper, or at a food co-op or organic grocery. College towns and larger cities are especially good areas to target.

Similarly, raising hogs and beef for local sale can be a moneymaker for you. If you raise a few hogs to butchering size—200 to 250 pounds—you can provide your own meat as well as find a market locally with folks who want meat that they know was raised close to home. Beef steers raised to about 800 to 1100 pounds will sell well. You should be able to easily sell halves or whole steers, especially if you can offer hauling to the custom slaughterhouse.

Garden produce, fruit, herbs

We have had success in selling garden produce and plants during the spring and summer. In fact, the demand for these items was really more than we could supply with the small home greenhouse that we have. There is great potential here, for a lot of people want sturdy homegrown plants and will pay a bit more for them. Timing is important when producing garden and bedding plants. That is, plan so that you have prime and healthy plants ready when they are most wanted by the buyers. You can market them right from

Growing garden and bedding plants in a home greenhouse can bring in extra money.

your home, or from local grocers or other retail outlets. Grow varieties that are popular locally.

Sell surplus strawberries, raspberries, blackberries, apples, cherries, peaches, and other home-raised berries and orchard fruit with a simple advertisement in your local newspaper, an ad tacked up at a local store, or just by word of mouth. Consider marketing these items at a farmer's market to help get better prices. In a similar fashion, home-grown herbs, both fresh and dried, can be a moneymaker for you. Some folks are having good success marketing specialty herbs directly to restaurants. Others sell to supermarkets, food co-ops, and organic groceries.

Furniture

One of my neighbors is an accomplished furniture maker. While he does have a nice little building where he could work, it is not surprising to know that it is crammed to the rafters with lumber, old furniture pieces, supplies, and such. He builds each of his pieces right out in the yard. We have some of his work here in our home: a pie safe, a jelly cupboard and a small bench. He makes solid, functional furniture and also displays his work at the annual festival in town, selling out every year. If you are talented in this area, you will find no shortage of buyers for your work.

Photography

One new business that recently started up in town is a small photography studio. Portrait photography has a rather limited market in this area, but even in our small community, high school senior class photos alone could pretty well keep a photography studio in business. Photographing weddings are another good source of work. Christmas portraits are another big seller. Other special occasions and holidays keep this photographer plenty busy. This is an area where, once your reputation for good work has been established, you will be able to keep busy.

Design and print shop

Out in the countryside 10 miles from where I live, a family has a high-tech, state of the art printing shop. Not the ordinary shop where only simple business cards and stationery orders are filled, this business designs, lays out and prints booklets, brochures, pamphlets, and magazines. Another branch of the family just down the road fills similar orders for books—both hard and soft cover—and magazines. I got a tour of the place a while back and was amazed to find in the plain nondescript buildings, top-notch computers running the latest in publishing software. The printing is done on computer driven presses worth a quarter of a million dollars. Not only do both of these families fill local orders, but the religious books, magazines, and tracts they publish are mailed all around the world. A smaller scale version of such a business may fit your pocketbook.

Wildcrafting

Out in the woods, there are folks who eke out a good deal of spending money by wildcrafting. The gathering of roots such as goldenseal, ginseng, mayapple, bloodroot, wild ginger, and other botanicals provides employment for a good many folks in rural areas where the plants are found. In addition, they can find a ready market for blackberries, raspberries, persimmons, mushrooms, and other wild foods. Even sassafras root and bark have a market.

Firewood

Similarly, a few fellows make pretty decent money by cutting firewood. The finest hardwoods in the world grow in our area: white oak, hickory, black oak, and ash. They also make the best firewood as well. Tops left from logging operations usually provide plenty in the way of cordwood. Some woodcutters obtain slabs and other leftovers from area sawmills. In this area woodcutters usually sell by the pickup load and get $25 to $35 per load. With a good chainsaw and a sturdy pickup truck, you'll be in business.

Rocks

Speaking of heavy work, there are a few stout fellows who are making some hard-earned money by harvesting stone. That's right, plain old "crick rock." They are simply picking rock from some streams, dry branches, and rocky hillsides and selling it for $30 to $40 a ton depending on the demand and the general shape of the stone. The rock may end up as veneer on a basement or house, as a hearth and chimney in a city-dweller's "country" home, or as a plain old rock wall. Especially large stones, weighing several tons apiece, may end up in someone's front yard as what we call a "status rock."

Hunting/fishing guide

Don't rule out the possibility for working as a hunting or fishing guide. In some states, guides are required for nonresidents hunting big game. Even in areas where they are not required, hunters are often willing to pay good money for the chance to bag game or catch a stringer of fish. In our area, guiding wild turkey hunters is catching on and some fishing guides are finding work on the area reservoirs. Hunting and fishing guides are licensed in some states, so check with your state fish and wildlife agency for more information.

Odd jobs

Performing plain old day labor is an honest way to earn a dollar. There are more than a few people in my area who do just that. They hire out by the day to do general labor whether cutting brush, building fence, painting barns, mowing, rough carpentry, or just about anything else that needs done. They are normally paid at an hourly rate ranging from minimum wage to a dollar or two above that, although some jobs may pay more.

Artist/writer

Another area resident transplanted himself and his family here about 25 years ago. Since that time, he has devoted his time to painting, writing, and photography. He has painted a mural in the lobby of our post office and has had showings of his paintings in several area galleries. His most recent successes have included four books about the local area. The first book highlighted local folk artists from the county. The second chronicled, in word and pictures, the daily life in our rural county. His third book was an ambitious, and successful, photographic history of the county. His fourth project was a collection of folk tales and stories of growing up told by dozens of old-timers in the area. His most recent project involved traveling around the southern half of the state, recording and documenting the last of the small-town country stores, drive-in restaurants and theaters, and similar businesses. This gentleman has done a lot for preserving the rich history of our area, and has made a decent living as well.

Another artist is a lady who lives away out from town and does sketches and pen and ink drawings of area landmarks. She often watercolors some of the prints of her work and offers all of them for sale at craft fairs, festivals, and in some local shops. Like the fellow above, she has also done much to record the rich tapestry of local country life and to record many of the local landmarks.

Wildland firefighter

During the summer months, I have used vacation time from my regular job and worked as a wildland firefighter. This adventuresome work has taken me to many fires in half a dozen states. Firefighting is not easy work. It is dirty, often dangerous, and physically demanding—a lot of "grunt" work. But it pays well. It is also satisfying, exciting, interesting, and offers an opportunity to see places you might not otherwise see. You will need to contact your local state or national forest office for more information in getting the necessary training and certification for this work.

Woodcarving

An acquaintance of mine is in the middle of marketing the works of his booming woodcarving business. After a few years of gaining

38

recognition and awards in state and regional carving contests, some major national organizations are now promoting and selling his work. The growing demand for his lifelike carvings of trout, smallmouth bass, and other fish have recently required him to travel to Galway, Ireland, to make sure the reproductions were being made to his satisfaction. Obviously this is not something that all of us could pursue, but if you have a knack for carving, there is a demand for good work.

Welding

An older fellow in town has a good welding business based at his home. He is probably one of the best welders around. He does have a portable, truck-mounted welder with which he makes runs for farmers and others needing on-site repairs, but he does the majority of his work at his shop, adjacent to his home. Good welders are hard to find. In fact, this old boy could be retiring in a few years, and I don't know of anyone planning to take his place.

Tax preparation

With the complexity of the tax laws, it is not surprising to learn that there is plenty of business in tax preparation. With some of the quality computer software available, this could be an area with promise for a home-based business.

Firearms

A friend of mine has a thriving gun shop located in a small building adjacent to his house. In addition to selling firearms, ammunition, and related equipment, he does some simple gunsmithing, i.e., minor repairs, fits scopes and accessories, and sights in firearms for customers. His location is out in the sticks off the beaten path, but he has a pretty steady line of customers including a lot of regulars.

Computer tech

It seems like every nook and cranny of the countryside has been affected by the computer age. Rural folks are jumping aboard the

Internet and finding worlds opening up with the stroke of a key or two. Even in these rural areas, some enterprising and talented persons are making good money by selling and setting up computer systems. A fellow I know recently quit his factory job after 20-some years and went full-time into this business. He did not simply plunge into the new business, but eased into it gradually, doing it as a part-time endeavor for several years. He knows his business and is swamped with customers.

Selling on the Internet

Computer-based sales is a booming business. Selling individual items over the Internet, notably by using the popular eBay, can be a real moneymaker. It is simple to become a registered seller on this web-based market. Rules and conditions are spelled out at their website.

Fixing cars

There are more than a couple of automobile body repair shops in the local area. They are required to work with several insurance companies when doing most accident repairs, but this helps to insure prompt payment. They are all kept busy and are making decent money. Related to that are the numerous automobile mechanic shops that dot the area. With the coming of increasingly inexpensive computer technology, good mechanics are able to branch out and obtain the diagnostic equipment needed to work on late model computer-laden vehicles. Furthermore, in rural areas such as ours, there are plenty of (t)rusty older vehicles to work on as well.

Craftsmen

A couple of fellows I know turn out some excellent woodcraft items. One fellow, retired from his previous job, does fine scrollwork and creates clocks, miniature houses, and similar pieces. Another friend, who also happens to be our county sheriff, creates jewelry boxes from native wood, inlaid with shell and polished to a fine finish. Both of these craftsmen are kept busy filling orders for their work. Still another acquaintance has switched from making inlaid wooden chessboards to handmade cigar humidors. His tip is to follow the trends, concentrate on what is popular at the time, and fill the niche with a quality product.

Flowers

Back in town, a small but thriving flower shop has a healthy business. They supply cut and dried flowers, plants, special occasion balloons, and similar items. They keep their van on the road delivering orders all over the area. Related to this, you may want to consider growing fresh and dried flowers for sale. Flower shops and craftspeople use large but varying quantities of those materials in their work and will normally jump at the chance to get good locally grown stock that has not had to travel over hundreds of miles.

Legal reporter

One enterprising lady uses her secretarial skills and her home computer to run her own business as a legal recorder. Her work takes her to the adjacent counties at times, where she records legal proceedings, meeting minutes, and other official records. At home, she transcribes them and provides her clients with neat, bound copies of the records. She makes a good income doing this work. A good word processor and good dictation skills are a must for this work.

School bus driver

A husband and wife each have their own school bus route. These routes are let for bid every couple of years and there are usually two or three people who bid on each route. These routes are usually not a sole source of income for most of the drivers, but are used to supplement some other employment.

Bulldozer/backhoe

There are several fellows I know who keep busy with their bulldozing and backhoe services. It seems that someone is always wanting a pond constructed, a lane put in, a ditch cleaned out, or something along that line. A couple of them also have dump trucks and can haul gravel and fill dirt. Another has a small ditcher for laying water and electrical lines and putting in drain tiles and the like. The initial cost of equipment for these types of operations can be rather intimidating, but the returns are pretty good. Rates of $65 to $100 an hour are not uncommon for dozer operators.

Electrician

There are a couple of local electricians who keep busy doing residential and commercial work. They do just about anything a person would need in the way of electrical work. One of them is also trained in installing and maintaining heating and cooling equipment.

Painter

One family is kept busy doing residential and commercial painting. They do everything from painting windows to doing entire factory buildings. That is one key to their success. They are versatile and they do good work at a reasonable price.

Office cleaning

Another local family makes good money doing office cleaning in area communities. This work is performed mostly after hours and not only do the husband and wife work at it, the teenage children also pitch in.

House cleaning

Another local lady supplements her family's income cleaning residences. She is trustworthy, does good work, and is kept as busy as she wants to be. There is a big demand for home cleaning in many communities. Many people are looking for honesty, in addition to a good job. If you get the reputation of being an "honest" house cleaner who does a good job, you can start a good business with a house cleaning service.

Building

A couple of men in town have teamed up to do carpentry and building log homes. Not only do they build the log homes, they cut the logs for the structure themselves on their bandsaw mill. When they are not putting up a cabin, they are kept busy with general carpentry jobs. With the mill, they can also move it right onto a property and custom cut lumber for the landowner at competitive prices.

There are several ads in the pages of *Backwoods Home Magazine* for the saw mills. It's a sizable initial investment, but is a sound long-term investment in a job.

Lawn service

One friend, his wife, and teenage son spend nearly every summer evening mowing lawns. He has invested in a really nice commercial grade riding mower and some solid push mowers and weed whackers. All three family members work hard and make decent money on this evening job.

This is another business where "word of mouth" will bring you all the work you want. "Dependable" is the reputation you need for success.

Tree trimming

I know of three different tree-trimming outfits in our area. They are kept busy doing home improvement work, clearing storm damage, and the like. One of the companies has expanded into doing landscaping and transplanting, and is doing very well. This type of work, however, does require a bit of traveling to larger population centers, as landscaping opportunities in our local area are pretty limited.

Auctioneering

Auctioneering is an area with good income potential for someone with the gift of gab. Estate auctions and farm auctions are held throughout the year, but particularly during the warmer months. Auctioneers are usually paid on a percentage basis. Once they have built their skills, much of their success depends on how well they publicize the sales to draw a good crowd.

Selling timber

The demand for good quality hardwood is high. Timber sales are not only a good forest management practice, but can provide a good sustained income for your property. Consult with your local state department of forestry to learn more about properly managing your woodlands for maximum value.

Christmas trees

Another form of tree farming is raising Christmas trees. Cut-your-own operations work well for many folks, especially when coupled with displays of other home-raised products and items. Consider spruces or pines adapted to your area.

Making a living anywhere is not easy. If you can make a go of it solely on your homestead, you are to be commended. If you need to get out and seek employment, then follow some of the tips given in this article. You do not need to give up on living in the backwoods though. Use your imagination, interests, perseverance, and skills. Find what is needed in your area and pursue that. Expand on something you already know how to do. Don't give up. Living in the sticks is worth it. 🌰

On the homestead

Baling and selling straw

By Steven Gregersen

Those of us who move to small rural communities often learn very quickly why they are small communities. Jobs are often low paying or nonexistent. Opportunities to make some "extra" money usually involve working for minimum wage at a task no one else wants. If you have access to the necessary equipment and find yourself needing some extra income, why not try baling and selling straw?

What began as an act of desperation for myself and a friend, eventually developed into a money making business. We each needed over one hundred bales of straw for our large gardens. But, after learning how much it would cost to buy the straw we decided to bale it ourselves. Even that didn't solve our problem completely. When people saw the straw stacked in the yard they would stop and ask to buy some for their own use. Next year, we vowed there would be enough straw for ourselves with plenty left over to sell.

If you want to cash in on this bonanza here's what you'll need: straw, basic equipment (tractor, baler, truck), storage for the straw, and a marketing plan.

How to secure the straw

We asked our wheat growing neighbors for permission to bale the straw left after the harvest. Most of the farmers in our area burn the wheat stubble so it was fairly easy to get permission to bale the straw after the harvest. We never had to pay cash for the privilege of baling the leftovers but we were always asked to provide straw for the property owner and be finished within a set time period. (This was

47

necessary in order to be sure there was time left to plant a second crop on the same field.)

Have your equipment ready

Have your equipment ready to go. Wheat sells best when it has been baled soon after the harvest. If it lays in the field too long it loses the bright, golden color. That will cost you money when you sell it. (Especially if the straw next to yours looks better.)

If you already own a tractor, rake, baler, and wagon (or truck), you're all set to go to work. If you don't have all the needed machinery your-self, try pooling your equipment with someone else (as I did). We split the straw and the expenses equally when the job was finished.

Storing the straw

Storage was our greatest problem. Unless you have a buyer to take the straw immediately you will need a place to store the straw. The best storage is a barn with a good roof and the walls covered on all sides. The next choice is a "hay barn" that has a roof but the sides are open. As a last resort you can use plastic or tarps to cover the straw. The last two methods will cost you money. Those bales exposed to the weather will discolor and eventually decompose. You will probably have to use them for mulch.

The storage area must also be accessible at all times of the year. You can't sell straw if you can't reach it due to snow or mud. Often your largest sales will occur when the weather is at its worst.

Marketing the straw

We sold the straw through three basic methods: classified advertising, weekly auctions at the county sale barn, and through the grapevine.

Classified ads brought results from local gardeners and pet owners. The straw was sold for $1.75 per bale if they picked it up. Extra was charged if it was delivered.

The country auction accounted for a large part of the sales at first. I worked within three blocks of the sale barn so it was simple to just bring in a pickup load of straw on Wednesdays (the regular sale day). The routine is fairly easy to follow. Unload the straw in the area reserved for selling straw and hay. Attach a note to one of the upper bales in the stack. The note should have your name, address, and phone number, plus the number of bales in the stack. When the straw is sold, the clerk records the price it brought. This record is turned into the office which will issue a check to you. The money can be picked up personally or it can be mailed to you the next day. There are two things to be aware of with this method. First, a commission is charged to pay the auctioneer. Second, unless you set a minimum price you'll take what it brings. If you do set a minimum amount and it doesn't bring that much, you must haul the straw home again.

The time of year makes a big difference in the price you get. Late fall and winter will bring the best rates. If you bring the straw in regularly, people soon expect it and the prices often improve because of increased competition among buyers.

The grapevine eventually became the most fruitful method. Once it become known we had straw to sell we had to be sure to save enough for our own use. Straw was sold to all types of people from those who bought only one bale for a few tomatoes, to farmers who bought up to three hundred at a time.

How much money can you make?

The amount of money you will make will vary according to your particular circumstance. Here is a breakdown to show how we did the second year (1987):

Total number of bales—850

Number of hours spent baling and hauling straw (20 hours each)—40

Cost of gasoline and twine—$40

The straw and expenses were split equally between the two of us providing four hundred bales each. (The property owner kept fifty bales for himself.)

My partner sold three hundred bales to a farmer for $1.50 per bale

($450 total). His profit was $430 for approximately 20 hours of work He kept 100 bales for his own use.

I sold 150 bales at an average price of $1.50 per bale for a profit of $215 after expenses. The tarp covering my straw was torn sometime during the summer. Even though rain ruined over half of the straw my profit still came to over $10 per hour.

These figures still do not take into account the straw we used ourselves and would have needed to buy from someone else.

Some final tips to increase profits

Your profit will depend on several factors. If the field and storage areas are close together you will have less traveling time and a greater profit per hour.

Wire-tied bales bring slightly more than twine-tied bales but wire costs more than twine. Ultimately, it won't make much difference which you use.

Be careful if someone wants to buy your straw by the ton. Straw is lighter than hay and it takes a large number of bales to make a ton. What might sound like a good price could cost you money.

Be quiet about the money you make! When the owner of our best field learned how much we made he went into business for himself the next year. ✿

Building beehives

By Gary Hutchins

Beekeeping as a business is ideal for the backwoods individual. Honey, beeswax, and pollen are easy to sell, and swarms of bees are free for the taking. The major drawback is the cost of equipment to house the industrious little creatures.

If you are interested in beekeeping but can't afford to buy commercial hive bodies and frames, here is a simple method of making your own beehives. This design is not only inexpensive, but it is also compatible with commercial equipment.

Building your own equipment is not as hard as it might seem. You can save hundreds of dollars while using scrap boards that seem to litter everyone's garage. The design of the equipment that is currently mass produced was developed over 75 years ago. During the early years of development a good quality wood glue was not available. The lack of a good glue made it necessary for the builder to use a locking joint in construction so that each joint could be held together securely with nails alone.

Since the advent of modern carpenter's glue, nails are used primarily to hold the joint together while the glue dries. Modern glues allow you to use basic joints and still achieve a joint that is stronger than the wood itself. You should use glue on all joints during assembly to ensure that your equipment doesn't fall apart while you are working your bees.

In the construction of bee equipment, a bee space of ¼ inch to ³/₈ inch is critical. If it is less than ¼ inch, the bees will fill the gap with propolis (bee glue). If it is greater than ³/₈ inch, the bees will fill the space

51

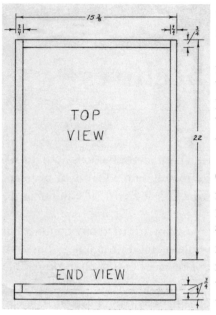

Figure 1

with brace comb. A space of ¼ inch give the best results.

Your equipment can be made from any scrap ¾-inch thick lumber that you have on hand. Plywood is great, even wafer board is good, but particle board tends to fall apart when it gets wet.

Start with your bottom board. Cut a piece of plywood (any thickness will do) $15^3/_8$ inches wide by 22 inches long. Now cut ¾ inch by ¾ inch lumber into two pieces 22 inches long and one piece 13¾ inches long. Now glue and nail all three pieces to one side of the plywood (see figure 1).

Now you can build the brood chamber. Start with ¾ inch lumber that has been cut into boards that are $9^5/_8$ inches wide. Cut two pieces $15^3/_8$ inches long and two pieces $19^5/_8$ inches wide. Take the two $15^3/_8$ inch pieces and cut a rabbet joint ¾ inch wide and $^3/_8$ inch deep across the grain on both ends. These rabbets are to allow you to join the boards to form a box. This joint minimizes the exposure of the end grain of the wood which slows the rotting process. Now on the same $15^3/_8$ inch boards cut a single rabbet joint $^5/_8$ inch wide and $^3/_8$ inch deep across the top. You can now assemble the brood chamber using glue and nails. Note: Be sure that the box is square before the glue dries (see figure 2).

The comb frames are the most complicated item in the hive, but this design is simple, rugged, and inexpensive. You will need ten frames for the brood chamber. Cut ¾ inch thick boards into ten $1^1/_8$ inch wide boards, each 19 inches long. These are your top bars. Next cut a ¾ inch wide by $^3/_8$ inch deep rabbet on both ends of the top bars. Now cut $^1/_8$ inch thick plywood (paneling or masonite works great for this) into strip $1^1/_8$ inches wide by 8¾ inches long. You will need twenty of these. These will be your end bars. Drill about four $^1/_8$ inch or smaller holes along the centerline (before assembly) so that you can wire in the wax foundation. The bottom bar is cut from ½ inch stock (¾ inch stock can be used in a pinch, but this reduces the brood area considerably). Cut 10 pieces $1^1/_8$ inches wide by 17½ inches long. Once all of your pieces are cut, glue and nail the frames together. Note: Be sure the frames are square before the glue dries (see figure 3).

There are several methods that can be used for spacing the frames. I have used two methods without any problems. The first method is to nail ¼ inch staples into the bottom of the rabbet on each end of the brood chamber, $1^1/_8$ inches apart. Start with one staple next to the sideboard. The second method requires two staples for each frame. These staples are hammered into the top bar on opposite sides, two inches from each end. These staples are left protruding from the wood ¼ inch, which spaces the frames.

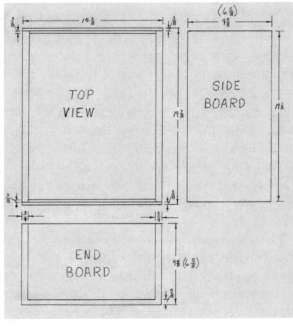

Figure 2

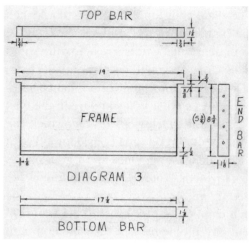

Figure 3

You will need to build three to six supers for each hive. Start with ¾ inch lumber that is 6⁵/₈ inches wide. Use the same directions as for building the brood chamber (see figure 2).

To build the frames for each super, use the same directions as you did in building the frames for the brood chamber, but cut the side bars 1¹/₈ inches wide and 5¾ inches long (see figure 3).

The inner cover allows you to use a telescoping top cover without the bees gluing it to the hive. Start by cutting a ¹/₈ inch thick piece of plywood or masonite 15³/₈ inches by 19⁷/₈ inches. Now cut ¾ inch thick boards into ¼ inch wide strips. Cut these strips into two 10⁷/₈ inch and two 13⁷/₈ inch long pieces. Glue these strips to one side of the plywood. Drill a hole one inch or larger in the center of the inner cover (see figure 4).

The sloping outer cover is the last item that you need to build. Start by cutting a piece of plywood 17³/₈ inches wide by 21⁷/₈ inches long. Cut ¾ inch by 1½ inch lumber into two strips 21⁷/₈ inches long and two strips 15⁷/₈ inches long.

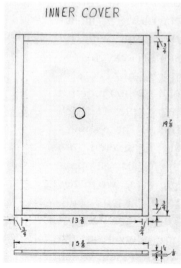

Figure 4

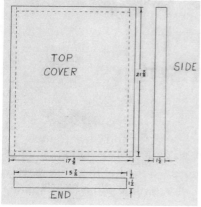

Figure 5

Glue and nail these pieces to one side of the plywood (see figure 5).

Cover the outer cover with aluminum sheet metal, tar paper, or whatever you have on hand that will shed water. You should paint the outside of your hive to protect it from the elements, but never paint the inside of the frames.

Building your own equipment not only saves you a lot of money, but you also become a little less dependent upon the commercial suppliers of bee equipment. Who knows, you may even find yourself making your own pollen traps, honey extractors, and smokers. It can be done.

[Editor's note: With the current bee populations imploding worldwide, making beehives and other aspects of beekeeping might prove to be very profitable if you are so inclined to learn about beekeeping.] 🐝

Saddle business

By Rosemary LeVernier

Cliff Stansell had had enough. He was tired of traveling, tired of being away from his home and his family, and tired of the daily rat race associated with working for someone else. So, he turned his lifelong interest in horses into a thriving home-based business.

Cliff, 40, is a tall, dark-haired custom saddle maker who is as much at home in his shop as he is the woods, working with horses, or playing the fiddle. His soft-spoken, easygoing manners put those around him at ease.

The "lack of people" drew him to northern Idaho from his native Gold Beach, Oregon in 1974. After moving to the small logging town of Priest River, Idaho, he worked at his trained profession of surveyor for many years. But surveying jobs took him all over the northwest, and away from home and his wife and two children for extended periods of time.

"I didn't want to do that anymore," he said. "I needed something that would keep me home and give me a livelihood—and something I wanted to do."

A saddle business seemed a natural choice for Cliff, who had worked with horses most of his life.

Saddle-making school

The nearest saddle-making course was in Spokane, Washington, a 90-minute drive in good weather. Five days a week for two years, Cliff made the 150-mile round trip commute from his home to Spokane Falls Community College, and spent six hours a day in class.

"You get out of it what you put into it," he said, "I figured this was going to be my livelihood, so I would go to school, then sometimes I'd go to a saddle shop after school to learn firsthand from other saddle makers. Then I'd come home every night and work until 10 or 11 o'clock every night."

He opened Stansell saddlery at a rented shop in downtown Priest River in 1984. Five years later, Cliff was ready to move the shop to his cabin 12 miles north of town in the woods, something he had planned from the start. "I figured I had to put in my time in town until I got established," he explained.

"Now, I don't get the walk-through traffic I got in town, which is good and bad," Cliff said. "It's bad because I don't sell little retail items or do repair jobs that I normally got in town. But it's good because I get my work done. In town, I was there 8 or 10 hours every day, and half of it was talking to people." With a chuckle, he added, "I like talking to people, but you have to get your work done too."

Photovoltaic power

The move home presented a problem—no electricity. For years, Cliff and his family used kerosene lamps, wood heat, and a propane stove and refrigerator in the log cabin they built. But some of Cliff's saddlery tools require power so he turned to the sun for a solution.

Now his 1,000 square foot cabin and 300-foot shop are powered with electricity produced from photovoltaic panels mounted on the cabin's roof. They turn sunlight into electricity, which is stored in 12-volt nickel cadmium batteries and run through an inverter to provide AC power.

"I wanted to stay off the (power) grid," Cliff said. "I wanted to be more self-sufficient and eliminate another monthly bill."

The solar system cost was far less than the $10,000 the utility company wanted to run in electricity from the nearest power line half a mile away. Winter's lack of sunshine doesn't worry Cliff. He simply plugs his batteries into his truck's alternator and lets it idle for a few hours each week to charge them.

"I didn't expect to have power, so it was a luxury when we got it," said Cliff's wife Betsy. "I couldn't do without it now," she laughed.

For daughter Katie, 12, electricity means listening to her favorite music, watching television and videos, and playing her electric keyboard. Son Ben, 6, is more interested in helping Pop than thinking about electricity.

The leather business

Out in the shop, where the stitchers, grinder, and lights hum along happily on sun power, Cliff shared a bit about his trade. "There's quite a price difference between good quality and poor quality leather, hardware, and saddle tools," said Cliff. "There's also a tremendous quality difference. To me, if you skimp on quality in the materials, then you're going to skimp on other things, too."

He uses leather tanned with bark instead of chemically-tanned leather which breaks down more quickly. "If you take good care of a saddle and the leather is good quality, then it'll last for 100 years easy," he said.

"I've got about 60 hours into a plain saddle," he said. "I'm a little bit slower than a lot of saddle makers, but if I went faster I'd probably be cutting corners. I'm more of a perfectionist."

Cliff's base price for a saddle is $1200. "I've seen factory made saddles for $250. I've got about $600 just into materials."

"I do the best job I can and I'm fair with the price," he said. "I think it's important to be a service to the community. When people lose that, they start ripping people off."

To a limited degree, Cliff has displayed and sold his handiwork at various horse shows. Now, his plan is to start selling more of his items at the working cowboy shows. He feels the shows will be a good source of potential clients. "The people who appreciate the quality of the work are the ones who use the stuff the hardest," he said.

He also plans to branch off into mail orders, and is currently putting together a catalog of his products. In addition to making saddles and doing repair work on saddles and leather items, Cliff's handiwork includes briefcases, chaps, gun scabbards, bridles, belts, knife sheaths, hatchet satchels, and family album covers.

Betsy helps her husband in the shop. "I do mostly finish work, like slicking and oiling saddles," she said. She also cleans saddles, does small repairs, braids leather, makes small items such as leather straps, and does the paperwork.

When not in his shop, Cliff can often be found working with his Percheron-class horses. He uses them for logging, haying, plowing snow, and riding. He enjoys working with the horses because it gets him out in the woods and moving around.

He's always willing to work out trades for his work. He once made a saddle in exchange for a truck, and has accepted building materials and labor in exchange for horse logging.

"To me, this is the ideal setup," he said, gazing out over the hayfields and forest visible from his shop. "A day where it's raining I can be inside doing leather work, and on nice days I can be outside working with the horses." 🌿

Cash from your crafts

By Dan and Becky Ames

The practice of self-reliant living often requires a person to do several different things in order to bring in needed cash. We've found that selling our crafts is an excellent way to generate income.

I make gifts and utility items from driftwood and hardshell gourds. Becky is the real artist in the family. She created "Thumbprint Originals," a line of handcrafted clay sculptures in miniature. The little animals, children, and scenes are always top sellers.

Participating in craft shows seems to be the most popular and well known method of selling crafts, and we've done a lot of them. It has been our experience that three or four good craft shows a year uses most everything that we can produce and provides substantial income.

Visiting with the people is one of the fun benefits of craft show selling. We've met lots of interesting folks this way. We get to demonstrate our crafts and talk to them about their crafts and their desire to sell them.

There are four questions from would-be craft sellers that we hear most often at our booth at craft shows. The answers to those questions may help encourage you to start a craft selling venture of your own.

How can I tell if my craft will sell?

First, a caution! Don't rely on the "ooohs and aaahs" of your friends or relatives as a reliable indication of your craft's acceptability and salability. These folks mean well. They wouldn't hurt your feelings for the world, so they won't be too critical or objective about your work. They may boost your ego, but they won't help your selling effort much.

There is only one way to find out if your crafts will sell. Submit them to the cold, impersonal eyes of prospective buyers in the marketplace! Participating in a craft show is the quickest way to test your craft's "salability."

If your craft is recognizable as a true craft, if it has original form and function, each piece well designed and crafted, if it is reasonably priced, you should find a ready market and willing buyers.

How do I get started selling at craft shows?

First, find a non-juried show near your home. Non-juried means that your work doesn't have to be judged. Anyone who pays the entry fee can show and sell.

Next, get acquainted with a fellow crafter who has done shows before. Ask around. My guess is one of your friends, or a friend of a friend, can be found to help you get started.

As an exhibitor, you will usually be required to provide your own table, chairs, and all the other trappings for your craft display. You should check and re-check to make sure you've taken everything you need for a good show. Do it before you leave home!

We suggest you make a list of all the things you need to take, and all the things you must do to get ready. After years of doing craft shows, we still make a list. It has saved our hides more than once!

There is a lot of packing and toting that goes along with doing a craft show. Don't worry. It won't be long until you've developed an easy system for moving your crafts and stuff from home to the show.

The type of show (indoors/outdoors), how many days you'll be there, and how far you must travel are just a few of the things you will need to consider in deciding what you must take. You will constantly change your "take and do" list, depending on the circumstances.

Take a person with you. If possible, find someone experienced at craft show selling to go along. Otherwise take a friend, relative, wife/husband, or your mother-in-law, but take someone with you! Don't try to do it alone, at least not the first one. You are going to need some help.

You will also need: table, chairs, display stands, your stock of craft items, nail apron or cashbox, money for making change, pad and pen, receipt book, string or small rope, scotch tape, pocketknife or scissors. Whew! What else?

Consider making the day as comfortable and pleasant for yourself as possible by taking: thermos for coffee or cold drink, doughnuts, lunch, small box of tissues, aspirin (or other needed medication), a spare set of car keys, sunglasses, tarp or other shade, rain gear, and plastic sheet to cover tables in case of rain.

Dress in layers so you can dress up or down as comfort and temperatures dictate. Take anything else you can think of that will help you have a really great day at the show.

How can I get the most sales for my effort?

The most important thing here is to stay involved. Once you get to the show and get your display set up, continue to stay involved in the selling activity. We are always amazed by people who put time, money, and effort into going to a show and then totally remove themselves from the selling activity!

For example, don't sit in the corner and read a book. We see this at every show. People have a built-in aversion to interrupting. If you're sitting there with your nose stuck in a book, you're going to miss a lot of sales.

Please, don't sleep! We attended a craft show last Saturday and saw this again! This old-timer had a really good display of grapevine wreaths and stick furniture. People were avoiding his booth like the plague. The crowd literally moved sideways around it.

When we got closer we saw why. The fellow was sitting in the shade in one of his beautifully handmade stick chairs—sound asleep! Great advertisement for the comfort of his chair, but no sales.

So, stay involved. There are many way to create interest and excitement for your craft display. Here are a few tips for you.

Use activity. Do something. Demonstrate making your craft. Create something beautiful right before their eyes! Carve the wood. Polish the jewelry. Sculpt the clay. Activity, especially during slow times, will get a crowd coming your way.

During the day you should arrange and rearrange the items in your display. Replace sold items with fresh stock. This will keep the display looking full. This is staying busy and involved with your showing and selling activity.

Use an attractive display. Put some thought and effort into how you display your items. They should be arranged neatly, not just stacked about. Always use a large, sturdy table for small and medium-sized items. Large items may be arranged on the floor (ground) around the table. Make it easy and fun to shop your booth.

Use attitude. Pleasant/friendly/positive, these are three big, important keys to your successful craft selling. Do it! Whether the sales have been good or not, whether the weather is lousy or not, whether you feel like it or not, do it. This will put cash in your jeans!

Use show and tell. I do, where it's appropriate. Remember the old time circus barker, "Step right up Ladeeze and Gentlemen!?" Well, just refine that a bit and it still works. As people pass in front of your display, hold up one of your craft items and call attention to some interesting feature about it. I absolutely guarantee you'll have a crowd. I have personally seen folks run toward my spiel and gathering crowd.

How can I sell crafts other than at craft shows?

When most folks think of selling crafts, the big four come to mind. Craft shows (fairs, festivals), a retail outlet of your own, consignment, to retail outlets of wholesaling. The last three on this list are good possibilities, but can be time consuming and expensive.

Over the years, we have developed and tested many different, successful methods for selling crafts. We've been asked so many times, "How do you do this, or that." So, we've collected all this information and written it into a report that helps experienced as well as beginner craft sellers get more cash from their crafts.

While the report goes into detail with helps for the standard method of selling, it also lists many alternative ways to sell crafts. The information shows you how to either sell crafts directly or to get exposure in the marketplace which leads to sales. Here are a few.

Use your local library. This is an excellent way to get exposure for your crafts. Call or visit the Head Librarian. Get an appointment to show samples of your work. You may be allowed to create an attractive display for the lobby area. In our town, we're usually allowed to leave it up a week or two. In three or four months do it again.

Ask for the library promotions calender and plan your display around their special emphasis. This becomes the theme for your display. Example: Native American Week, use Indian designs on wall hangings, pottery, etc.

You may or may not be allowed to price your work for this display. Ask the librarian what their policy is. You may show a neatly lettered sign of your business card, so folks can contact you.

When you remove your display, be sure to thank the Librarian. Establish a good relationship with her and you will be invited again.

Bank lobby areas are excellent for getting exposure for your work. Sales will be generated by bank customers who pick up one of your prominently displayed business cards.

Contact the bank services representative, show your samples, and discuss the type of display you have in mind. Be open to this person's ideas and incorporate them where possible. The bank will be happy to display your work as a "customer service." You've helped the bank with unusual decoration and a point of interest for its customers.

Contact your local County Extension Agent for information about Home Demonstration Units (HDU). You may be able to arrange to teach your crafts and may charge students a reasonable fee for instruction and materials. Classes usually meet at an HDU designated place one or two evenings a week for four or five weeks.

Be sure to plan your instruction carefully. Good communication skills are a must. The goal should be for each student to have mastered the principles of your craft and to have completed at least one item (project) by the end of the course.

Your local HDU chapter schedules many community activities and the director may suggest other ways you may participate. You may not always be able to actually sell your crafts at a particular event, but the exposure you'll get will be priceless!

Get acquainted with your Avon lady. These ladies have regular established customers and routes that are valuable to them. While they can't usually sell your crafts, they may be willing to take you along when they make their visits and introduce you to their customers.

Take along a few samples of your crafts for a brief presentation and take orders for future delivery. You'll want to deliver and collect on your own time. Don't bother the Avon lady with this. Be sure to offer her a 10% commission on every sale you make.

Remember to include your business card with each order you deliver and ask for referrals from your new customer (their friends or relatives who might be interested in owning one of your crafts).

This method works well with any direct salesperson in your area, Mary Kay Cosmetics, McNess Products, and Stanley Home Products are all possibilities.

Life is for the living! Selling your crafts will be a great little adventure for you. You will meet some interesting people and make some lasting friendships. Some of the nicest people we have ever met are craftpersons. We hope you will give it a try. 🌢

Firewood business

By Dan Shechtman

*M*y interest in firewood began in the late 1970s. There I stood with my young wife, new baby, and first home contemplating the oncoming Pennsylvania winter. Upon taking inventory of my assets which included a strong back, a well-broken-in pickup truck, and a bent toward self-sufficiency, it became clear that if we were to stay warm that winter and not go broke, a woodstove would have to replace the oil furnace in our home.

Armed with a 42-inch swede saw and a poll axe I cut, split, and burned seven cords of wood that first winter. I had found my calling.

For the next few years my wood pile steadily grew. I was cutting more than I needed and the rows of firewood threatened to swallow what was left of our yard. I faced a crisis—if I didn't find an outlet for my surplus we would soon vanish under the wood pile. Ceasing to cut was out of the question. The light bulb went on in my brain and a business was born.

Within five years I was handling for my own use, and delivering to customers, between 50 and 60 cords per year. Needless to say things happened quickly. Since those first cuts with the swede saw almost 15 years ago, I have learned a thing or two about the firewood business.

Enthusiasm a must

To make it in the firewood business one needs enthusiasm and equipment. Enthusiasm results from the union of necessity and romance. If you are well off and just need a little exercise don't commit to a business. It demands too much. To do it right you need to be cutting in mid-July and in the dead of winter as well as those "crisp clear autumn days." If the smell of oak or ash or tar chain oil doesn't turn you on, you need to find another line of work that does touch your soul. But if you feel that you are a timber cutter about to happen, read on.

Good saw (or two) essential

In order to cut wood in sufficient quantity to sell, a first rate, commercial duty chainsaw is essential. Two is even better because unless you are a top notch mechanic with all the parts you need, you will experience, sooner or later, down time you can't afford. The saws should be of the same make and bars and chains should be interchangeable.

Maybe, in this ideal world, one saw would be new and the other—the spare—would have been reconditioned by a chainsaw service mechanic.

An adequate saw should be between 3.3 and 5.0 cubic inches. This range should accommodate most physiques and pocketbooks and will comfortably carry a 20-inch bar. Unless you are into some monster trees, a 20-inch bar is all you need. It can cut up wood of almost 40 inches in diameter and still be handy for homestead chores.

The saw—new or used—should be equipped with an anti-kickback device; a chain brake or bar tip cover, and should come from a chainsaw dealer who services what he sells. Make sure the dealer will stand behind his product.

New or used, don't buy it until you run the saw hard. It should start quickly and smoothly, and it should cut with power and snap. If it doesn't, don't compromise; buy the next one up, because 100 cords from now you will be glad you did.

Shut the saw off and make sure that the bar is well oiled and the oiler pumps like crazy. Start it again. Warm, the saw should fire right up. If the saw is used check the air filter. It should look good and clear.

Buy your saw from a service dealer close to you. A great buy on a super saw from a dealer whose saw brand is not in your area is not a deal. Saws need service; you want to be close to that service.

Stihl, Husquavarna, Jonsereds, and Sach Dolmar are the top of the line saws. Olympik, Echo, and Poulan are also excellent and less expensive. I own an Olympik and I love it. Those old American stand-bys—Homelite and McCulloch—have sold out to the department store set. To their credit Homelite does continue to make their model super XL as does McCulloch with their Mac 700. These two models are rugged and worthy. The rest of their line, in my opinion, is not.

Know your saw

Before you venture into the woods know your saw. Know how to maintain it, know how to sharpen the chain, and know how to work safe. Read the manual and be able to quote it chapter and verse. A chainsaw in experienced hands is an amazing tool, but it is unforgiving and can maim or even kill.

Maul vs. hydraulic splitter

Now that your wood is cut it must be split. A few years ago the market was deluged with new and innovative splitting devices. Ninety-nine percent of them were junk. Wood is split by driving a wedge into a log causing the log to cleave along its natural grain. This wedge can be powered by muscle or by a hydraulic ram powered by a gasoline engine or a tractor PTO.

The old standby wedge and sledge is supremely effective for producing enough firewood for one's own needs, but it is too slow for commercial application. I use both splitting maul and a large hydraulic splitter. Both tools are useful in their place.

The hydraulic splitter is not that much faster than the splitting maul, nor is it easier. You merely trade one type of exertion for another. But the hydraulic splitter enables me to accept large wood, knotty beech, and stringy elm and not give it a second thought. The splitting maul, on the other hand, splits my oak and ash and allows me to travel light on forays where this straight-grained wood is the quarry.

Hydraulic splitter

My hydraulic splitter is made by Giant Vac and is big, sporting a 12 hp Kohler engine that puts out 20 tons of push. If a splitter has a two-stage pump, the necessary 15-20 tons of push can be had from engines with as little as 5 hp.

My Giant Vac has certain traits which one should look for in any hydraulic splitter.

It has a 10 inch wedge which is a real time saver in the big wood.

It has a long rail and tang which enables me to push and pull it around myself. Because of this long tang the weight is well balanced and dragging the splitter into woods, over rough ground, is not a problem.

I have used smaller splitters which were much harder to maneuver due to poor weight distribution. I like the big tires on my splitter for highway towing. I do wish I had a two-stage pump on it however; this would help the efficiency of the stroke.

I paid $1100 for this splitter, used in 1986. Commercial splitters ain't cheap. If you are mechanically able, get a hold of the Northern Hydraulics catalog. They sell parts for the do-it-yourselfer. Not a bad way to go—build your own!

Splitting maul

I still split about $1/_3$ of my wood with a maul. I have great regard for those pipe handled monsters on the market and I used one for years. Eventually the stiff pipe handle made my elbow a disaster area. My present maul is your basic 8 pound head on a hickory handle, and on the right wood I can split and stack in the truck a full cord in about two hours. Good for the wallet and good for the body and spirit. Don't forget your wedge, just to make that first crack in that big oak round.

There is a guy 40 miles north of me who splits 800 cords a year with a monster maul. He handles all oak and leaves the crutches and knotty rounds where they lie. Still—wow! He was described to me as "a real man."

The right truck

A pile of cord wood is a beautiful sight. Stand back; admire your work. But now it has to be transported. I have a Ford F250 heavy duty pickup.

It can carry a full cord of green oak, and it is the minimum vehicle for the commercial cutter. I wish it dumped; that would save me hours every week unloading. I wish it were four-wheel drive; I could then leave my come-along home. I wish the bed were closer to the ground; those big rounds get heavy, and the higher you lift 'em the heavier they seem. On balance the truck is a fine compromise for my needs as it also takes my wife to the market, the kids to school, and me over the road in search of adventure. Life is a balancing act and most of us require multi-purpose equipment which accommodates all the aspects of our lives.

I have seen excellent trailers made from old pickup beds. This is another way to go as the trailer fits nicely into the overall scheme of self-sufficient living without forcing the owner to commit to a specialized vehicle.

The firewood business is a business of personal contact. You will be judged by your product. Sell generous cords of good, seasoned wood. I have found that the species of wood, within certain limits, is less important than how well seasoned it is. Better dry Norway Maple than green oak.

Buy the best, heaviest duty equipment you can afford. Understand how to use and maintain it and prepare for a wonderful journey. I wish you luck and safe cutting.

Resources

1. Baileys Catalog, Super Source for about every wood cutting need, P.O. Box 550, 44650 Hwy 101, Laytonville, CA 95454. www.baileysonline.com, 800-322-4539

2. Crosscut Saw Co., P.O. Box 787, Seneca Falls, NY 13148. catalog@crosscutsaw.com, 315-568-5755

3. Northern Tool and Equipment, 2800 Southcross Drive West, Burnsville, MN 55306. www.northerntool.com, 952-894-9510

4. *Chainsaw Savvy a Complete Guide*, by Neil Soderstrom, 1982. 🐾

This country job ROCKS!

By Charles A. Sanders

Down here in the hills and hollers of southern Indiana, there is rock a'plenty. Old farm fields still show evidence where early farmers gathered and piled the countless rocks that got in the way of their plows and harrows. Rock bluffs and cliffs abound. Who knew that the rocks our ancestors fought on the farms and tossed into piles would become a marketable commodity? Charla and Richard Ivey and their family have learned just that and have built a good business upon those rocks.

Charla had a medical condition that required her to quit her factory job. She wanted to do something to bring in some money and to teach the kids how to develop good work habits. Basically, she drove the truck and the kids threw the rock onto the truck. She helped all she could and decided she enjoyed it too.

After doing it this way for a couple of years and selling rock to a nearby dealer, Charla decided to get serious and start her own business. It wasn't until I began work on this article that I learned they had named their business "Backwoods All Natural Stone." Quite appropriate, I think.

They started with just a pickup truck and a crowbar. A hand-crank boat winch mounted in the back of the truck helped to pull large boulders up a couple of planks and into the truck.

Eventually, once they decided to go full-time, they bought a "Bobcat" loader and a dump truck. Charla stated, "It was kind of scary at first. I wasn't sure that I wanted to spend that kind of money." But after serious consideration, they decided to buy the equipment and go to work.

Richard was already familiar with stone as a source of income. He is employed at Indiana Limestone, where he works in the limestone quarry and operates heavy equipment. He works there 8 to 12 hours a day, then comes home to help Charla and the kids. The kids all help. Kayla, 18, is a senior in high school, has a strong work ethic, works with mom part-time, and also at a local pizzeria. She is active in high school as a varsity cheerleader, and is on the high school track and cross-country team. Tim is 16 and in addition to helping with the stone business, is active in high school and is on the varsity cross-country team. Even young Jacob, 6, helps where he can and will soon be an active member of the family team.

Finding stone

This is possibly the most important part of the whole business. They merely ask around of folks who have suitable acreage with a large supply of rock.

Some folks readily allow access. Others worry about the later effect of washing or flooding. When working on an individual's property, Charla and her crew are careful to:

• Not strip the area of stone, leaving sufficient rock to provide natural waterflow.

• Replace and reset stones in areas where they created access lanes.

• Fill spots where they removed partially exposed stones from the ground.

• Occasionally create a small dam or water bar to also help divert the waterflow.

In short, they always take good care of the properties where they are allowed to harvest stone—filling holes and keeping streams and drainages in good shape.

They will occasionally go into an area just after a logging operation. During the course of the logging operation, the skid trails that were created also provide good access to get to stones on the tract of land. The log skidders also usually unearth quite a bit of marketable stone during

73

the making of the trails and while dragging out and yarding logs.

Here is a required caveat for potential rock harvesters—be sure to check the legalities of harvesting stone in your area. Laws differ from state to state, and place to place. In our area, it is legal to harvest stone on private property with the permission of the landowner. However, most all of the state and federal lands are off-limits to rock harvesting. This includes state and national forests.

In most cases, the stone is merely picked up and loaded either into the truck or into the loader bucket. Some rocks require the use of a spud-bar to help pry it from the ground. They sometimes use their Bobcat loader to help lift some of the really large, partially buried stones from the ground. It is also used to move the stones into the truck for hauling back to the yard.

Finding customers

Charla began her business by selling to a larger dealer nearby. She operated in this way for about a year before deciding she could do better eliminating the middle man by selling directly to customers.

She knew a few of the customers where her stones were already going, so she contacted them and asked to sell to them directly. This arrangement has worked out well; they seem to have met in the middle. She gets a better price than she would by selling the stones to the "middleman." In turn, the customer is paying less than he was. Charla told them up front to keep buying from the original supplier, but to give her a try. They soon became full-time customers who like the personal attention and the quality of the material that the Iveys supply.

The Iveys now have five full-time customers and three part-time customers. All but one are professional landscapers, the other is a concrete and material supplier. They keep the Iveys really busy filling orders for large stone and landscape rock that, in turn, goes out to construction and landscape sites all over the area.

Here are some ideas that helped Charla develop a good customer base:

• She looked through the phone book for landscapers, builders, and suppliers. She then followed up with a call or a personal visit.

• Word of mouth has also helped in developing her customer base.

• Charla maintains a photo album showing various aspects of her stone harvesting business, along with photos of stone sample sizes, types, etc. She also has photos of some of the landscaping jobs she and her family has done. The album helps to visually sell her products and budding landscaping services.

Charla told me that she wants to keep the business rather small and not have to worry about employees and all the headaches that go along with them. She has half a dozen good customers that include suppliers. Those customers pretty well buy all the stone the Iveys can supply. Charla would be happy to develop the customer base just a bit, perhaps building up to 12-15 steady customers.

Even staying small, she still has the same worries as most other small business owners, including customers, taxes, her few employees (family), sources for materials, deliveries, and equipment.

The family has begun to branch out a bit into doing some landscape jobs, jobs in which natural stone figures prominently. The sideline seems to mesh nicely into the rock harvesting business. The landscape jobs have just been picked up here and there as they have time.

Selling the stone

Their customers have used this local "crick rock" on projects as far away as 80 miles.

Here is what their customers are looking for:

• Good solid rock that isn't going to shatter or crumble.

• Some landscapers really like the rocks that have a lot of moss on them.

• Others prefer rock that has a lot of pits in it.

Their main rock product is stone that runs from 18-36 inches in length and from 150-2500 pounds. The stone is marketed as "field stone" or "creek stone."

They usually bring their rock into the yard, where the stone is sorted by size and type. Then it is "palletized" or loaded onto wooden pallets. To contain all this loose stone on a pallet, a wire cylinder is first created and attached to an ordinary wooden pallet using woven fence wire and fence staples. For small stone, 2 x 4 welded wire is used to make the cages. The cylinders are then filled with sorted stone for the particular customer. Each pallet of big boulders usually holds about 1500-2300 pounds of stone, but some individual large rocks will weigh as much as 3000 pounds.

Large irregularly-shaped boulders are used for landscaping, rock gardens, water gardens and as "status rocks." Those are the ones you see out by the driveway that are about as large as a VW Bug and have landscaping and flowers planted around them.

Smaller flatter stones that are 3-5 inches wide and 1-6 inches thick are used for everything from planting beds to veneer on new building construction. Flat stone is desirable for stepping stones and veneer.

One customer really likes the old hewn foundation stone that is found all over much of rural America. The old stones were originally simply hewn into a roughly rectangular or wedge shape and were used to support houses, barns, and homestead outbuildings of all types. In many places throughout our country, these old stones are all that remain of a once-thriving homestead. Charla's customers will pay higher prices for these hewn, shaped stones, so she is constantly on the lookout for them.

Charla enjoys her business, even though it involves hard work and often long hours. She says it has taught her kids how to work hard and deal with customers. 🐂

Buying & selling used books

By Mary Kenyon

Do you love books? Do you enjoy hunting for the treasures amongst stacks of books at auctions, thrift stores, or library book sales? Want a business you can run from your home? Then the book business might be just what you're looking for.

Our home business selling books has been flourishing since the closing of our used bookstore in November 1997. Eight shelves of books line our living-room and office walls, alongside the three that contain our personal collection and home-schooling books. As homeschoolers and strong believers in learning from "real" books versus textbooks, we are perfectly content being surrounded by our product. While our home business venture started out as part of a small business that was pared down to come home, this type of business would work for anyone with a little book knowledge, time for book-hunting, and a good customer base.

The majority of our targeted customers are homeschoolers, though we do deal with a few collectors, other book-dealers, and some backwoodsy types who are always searching for out-of-print books on gardening, building homes, raising small livestock, canning, and similar topics. I know book dealers who specialize in certain topics, and the same could be done in a home business, especially for someone hooked up on the internet for selling, which we are not.

Target your market

To get started in a home business selling books, you must decide who your customers are. We sell to homeschoolers because we are homeschoolers and we know what homeschoolers are looking for. As we are learning more about collectible juvenile books, we could feasibly branch out and sell to juvenile book collectors. At this point, however, I prefer to sell to families who are using these books for reading enjoyment, not shelving them just to own a complete collection. We know one bookseller who deals only with juvenile literature on the internet, and her prices have risen beyond the budgets of most homeschoolers we deal with. She has also gotten so busy and involved in her book business she put her own homeschooled children back in school so she would have more time for the business.

Are you a self-sufficient type who can spot a Rodale book on gardening halfway across the room at a library sale? Target this population and advertise in magazines or newsletters written for the back-to-nature crowd. Love history? What about history buffs who can't get enough pre-revisionist history books? Homeschoolers generally fall into this category too, which is why we can always sell the old history texts we unearth at auctions. Recently we profited $20 on a children's history book we bought for 50 cents at a thrift store. With beautiful pictures and stories, it was well worth the $20.50 we charged a special customer who is always searching for this type of book. Are you more into the collectible books, looking for special and first editions, and learning about current trends and values? Your customer base could be collectors, and ads could be run in collector's magazines.

Collecting inventory

Once you've decided your target customers, it is time to start collecting your initial inventory. Maybe your own library can be a starting point. I am just now, after three years, rebuilding our personal library, adding books we once owned or always wanted to own, after selling one-half our collection initially to help get our business going. Call local libraries to see when they will be having book sales, and attend every one within at least a 50-mile radius, searching for the type of books you want to sell. Prices are generally in the 50-cents to $1 range, and not all the books are ex-library (with markings that decrease their value). Auctions are another boon to the book-hunter. Twice we have bought an entire hayrack full of boxes of books for only $1. Yes, we ended up with a lot of worthless junk, but our initial investment netted some real gems, including an original McGuffey's reader and Ray's Arithmetic.

Be aware, however, that when books are mentioned individually in the auction ads, you may be competing with book dealers who will be willing to pay $100 for one book. Even when this happens, you may end up with boxes of beat-up books that can still be sold as reading copies if they are highly collectible authors or illustrators.

Thrift stores or stores that depend on donations for their stock are another great source for books. Hidden amongst the shelves of old book-club books and Reader's Digest Condensed books (virtually worthless to any book dealer) you can find beautiful out-of-print children's books or a collection of beautifully illustrated Bible stories for a client who wants such things.

Other book dealers can be a source of inventory, too, especially if they are dealing with a different clientele than you. I have found nice ex-library copies of books my customers want at bookstores for as little as $1, simply because they don't deal with ex-library as a rule, or the majority of their clients aren't interested in general juvenile literature from the 1950s, while mine are. I have many customers who will pay $3 for a nice-looking copy of a book they read as a child that they want to own for their own children.

During your book searches, don't turn away from good copies of books that you won't personally be dealing with. For instance, when I see beautiful art books in slipcases at thrift stores for $1, I buy them up even if I personally don't sell them. Why? Because I know a bookstore that gives me $5 in credit for each one I bring in. I have gotten more than $500 in credit at one particular store where I know what the owner is looking for. I use that credit, which easily equals five times the investment I put into it, and purchase books at his store that I know will sell on my list. By choosing carefully, my initial investment of $20 gets me $100 worth of their books which I can sell for $150—an end profit of $130.

When you have your initial inventory of at least 300-500 books, you need to make up a list of what you are selling. I number my books by category, ie, C1, Al, El for Children's, Adult's, and Educational), and I add and delete these numbers as books sell and as I add more onto the list.

I have seen many lists that are not coded but simply list the titles and authors of books available, sometimes dividing by author or subject.

I started my list with approximately 500 books total, and in three year's time it has grown to include almost 2000 books, the majority being children's and educational. I have two to three pages of back issues of highly-sought after back issues of magazines which changes quickly. You could feasibly do this list on a typewriter, but with the amount of books I have, it is nice to use a computer and make the print smaller so I can get more on each page. And updating lists is a breeze with a computer, deleting titles that sell and adding a new title in its place. This is more appealing than crossing items out as they sell.

Watch printing costs

Sending out your booklist to prospective customers can be expensive. The cost of printing your lists can quickly eat up profits, so compare prices. I have paid as little as 2-cents a sheet but now my 24-page, double-sided list is costing closer to $2 each to print and another $1.50 to mail. I now ask for $2 for prospective customers to receive a list, and regular customers are good about sending another $1—or 4 stamps—to help out so they can continue getting lists.

Advertising essential

Once you have your list, you need to advertise. Name your business, and, if you expect a lot of mail or want to look more business-like, rent a post office box. Working on a small budget, I searched for every free advertising space I could find, including review columns in various homeschooling magazines and newsletters. I also mentioned our business in every newspaper and magazine article I wrote and published, including this one. I ran a few paid ads but found personal mentions to be more beneficial in terms of eventual sales. A large proportion of people who request a list never buy, but the good repeat customers make up for them. Repeat customers are good about spreading the word, too, and at least one new customer a month comes from a satisfied regular customer.

When I get an order, I send a postcard or letter letting the customer know what is still available from their request list, how much their total is with postage added in, and let them know I will hold their books for them for 14 days. After I receive the money, I mail the books out bookrate. Approximately one out of 40 customers never pay, which is why I never delete a book from the list until it is paid for.

The time it takes

Our home business entails approximately 2 days a month for traveling on our "book hunts," and approximately 15 hours a week working on updating the list, filling orders, and packing boxes. I know book dealers who work many more hours than this each week and many of them are also dealing over the internet, but with homeschooling, caring for young children, and writing, 15 hours is enough of a stretch for me. Our children can help with some of this, and the entire family enjoys hunting books and are learning to discern between good books and junk. We figure this in as part of their homeschooling.

Don't want to get quite this involved in selling books? You can start small by selling to people like me. Get to know your local bookstore owner. What is he looking for? If he pays highly for war and history books, keep an eye out for these at book sales. If you can get cash instead of credit, you could feasibly make $4 or $5 off a book you paid $1 for. If no one else is bidding on old quality poetry and classic books at auctions, buy a box for $1 or two, clean them up, and try selling them to a book dealer that sells this type of book.

Personally, I am always looking for certain types of books and will pay cash for them. Because I sell ex-library books but am unable to attend every library book sale in the state (though I'd like to), someone could purchase all the Lois Lenski's, Landmarks, and Childhood of Famous Americans series books at 50-cents a piece and sell them to me for $1 to $4 each, profiting nicely.

Don't just buy up books, hoping someone would like them and give you cash for them, but find out what is being sought after. Maybe you already attend the sales for books for yourself but could spend a few more minutes searching for someone else, and pay for your books in the process.

How much can you expect to make in the book business? Of course, it depends on what kind of books you are dealing with, and how many people you can reach. Dealers on the internet can command higher prices, and dealers who sell to collectors can get more for their books, but the condition of the books is much more important than if you are dealing with customers who are just looking for good reading copies. Because we are constantly adding to our inventory, some months we only see a small profit of a couple hundred dollars. We've built up enough inventory that we could feasibly sell from our current list for months with new customers, but at this point 85% of our monthly sales are to regular customers so it is important to constantly add new stock to the list and to locate certain books we know these customers are interested in. If we were actively reaching out for new customers, our profits would increase exponentially. Selling books can be a nice second income and will always pay for itself as long as you know your market.

So, what are you waiting for, book-lovers? Get hunting and make some money off a product you love and believe in. The only thing you've got to lose is some space in your house. 🕮

Hay business

By Emory Warner

Making a living in the country is hard work. I see many good ideas presented in *Backwoods Home Magazine*—everything from telecommuting to handyman's services, and I would like to present another alternative: making hay. While no ticket to riches, (what is?) hay can give you a lump sum just prior to the fall and winter spending season.

Like any other business, nothing happens until something is sold. Before starting, survey your local area for a market. Direct sales to hay users will net the most profit, but are the most difficult sales to make. Auctions are an excellent place to sell your hay, the drawback being that you are at the mercy of supply and demand. I suggest that you talk, in person, to boarding stable operators, horse and beef farms, and one or two dairy operators to get a feel for the local market. I have found that the same hay will bring $2.50 to $3 a bale in one end of the county, and $1.25 at the other end. I have had poor success with those who advertise themselves as hay buyers. They either beat you way down on the price, or just plain don't pay. If you make good hay, the word will get out. Every rural community has a gathering place where everyone tends to congregate, and good quality hay producers will find themselves a frequent topic of discussion.

Getting started is not as difficult as it appears. Three things are necessary:

· Equipment
· Sufficient grass
· Storage

Equipment is not as costly as it appears, fields can be cut on a shares basis, and storage can be made up with discarded pallets and poly tarps. You can get started for about $5,000, less if you are willing to buy equipment in need of repair.

The major expense in equipment will be the tractor itself. You can easily upgrade equipment later if you have an adequate tractor. You'll need at least 35 horsepower, and 50 would be better to operate a baler and wagon. A low clearance, live Power Takeoff (PTO), and good brakes are essential. Diesel power is well worth the added expense, as you will quickly realize savings in reduced operating costs compared to gasoline. Expect to pay at least $3,000 for a useable tractor. If you're homesteading, you probably already have a tractor. If too small, trade in the little one for a bigger one.

Mowers are next in expense. If you can find one in good shape, buy a mower-conditioner or "haybine." Haybines run the cut grass through rollers much like the wringer on an old-fashioned washing machine, which cracks the hard stems, making the hay better due to its softer texture as well as helping the hay to dry more quickly and uniformly. Second and third cutting hay is much less "stalky" and can just as easily be mowed with a sickle bar. If you find a "hay conditioner," then a sickle bar mower alone will suffice. The conditioner is run over the first cutting hay, crimping it, and is not really needed for subsequent cuttings. Mowers run the range from "free for the hauling" to well over $1,000. Haybines can usually be found for $1,000 to $1,500. Hay conditioners run from "haul it away" to $1,000. Hayrakes run about $500 to $1,000. Find one in decent shape and pay the money; you'll save very little trying to repair a clunker. Side-delivery rakes have changed very little in the last 50 years, and they hold their value as a result.

Balers can be found at surprisingly low cost. Most commercial operators make hay into large round or 3'x3'x8' rectangular bales, so that the hay is handled efficiently by a front-end loader with a long spike. The older small square balers that make 18"x18"x40" bales are available anywhere for $600 or so with a drop chute, or $1,200 for a baler with a kicker.

Hay wagons are not optional. Chute balers can drop bales on the ground to be picked up later, but this is a waste of time. Towing a wagon behind the baler to catch bales is a far more efficient method. If you have a chute baler, you'll need someone on the wagon to stack bales as they come off the chute. A kicker baler will launch bales overhead and into the wagon mechanically, making baling a one-man operation. Flat wagons suitable for a chute job can be had for as little as $200. Rack wagons for a kicker will start at about $600. You'll have to look around a bit to get a good deal, and you'll need more than one.

Finding grass to make hay from is not too difficult. Obviously, start with your own land. Cutting other people's land is how most of us do it, and will fall into several categories. Absentee landowners, retirees', and city refugees on acreages frequently will give away whatever hay you make in return for mowing fields for which they have no use. Other homesteaders will usually accept half the hay made as rent. I pay my landowners 40% of my profit, with the understanding that any improvements will come out of my pocket. I don't like a 50/50 split of profits and expenses: profits are easy to expend, and expenses can sometimes be hard to collect, especially if you're dealing with an absentee landowner who sees no need for fertilizer, etc. Start out small, care for the land like it's yours, and you'll soon have landowners seeking you out.

Don't overlook storage of finished hay. I made this mistake and lost 80% of my first cutting. The best place to store hay is in your own barn if you have one. If not, finding a rental may be difficult. If you are lucky, one of your absentee or retired landowners will have a suitable building to rent for 10-cents a bale. Otherwise you'll have to stack your hay on pallets and cover it. This will work if you do it right. Make certain that there is room for air to circulate. Stack the bales in a pyramid shape, and use a large enough tarp to cover the hay right down to the pallets. Tie it down securely and use something to keep the tarps from lying on the top row of bales. Condensation will collect on the inside of the tarp and drip into the hay and ruin it.

I made a flat-topped stack, used poly to cover it, and didn't tie it down well enough. A gusty thunderstorm blew through and tore holes in the plastic that didn't blow away outright. Wet bales rapidly become moldy and are unfit for animal feed.

The only "secret" to making good hay is to dry it thoroughly after cutting and keep it dry. Hay that is rained on in the windrow will bleach out and lose much of its feed value. Hay baled too quickly will heat up, get moldy, and may even catch fire. Conditioned hay will cure in two days of sunshine; mowed hay will take three. Once the mowed hay is cured, rake it into windrows and bale it. Experience will quickly teach you how large a windrow to make for maximum efficiency of the baler. Good hay will have a green color and a sweet smell. Moldy hay will be dusty and smell musty. Avoid breathing the dust from moldy hay; it is a haven of mold spores and bacteria and will make you ill.

Your initial survey will aid you greatly in marketing your product. If you concentrate on making quality hay, attempt to capture some of the horse feed market. If you have a horse racing track nearby, start there. Take several sample bales, phone ahead for an appointment, and good luck. While you're out, locate any boarding stables, rental stables, etc. and try your luck. Bulletin boards in tack shops and feed dealers may help. I've gotten referrals from the local sawmill and from people picking up sawdust for bedding. Don't overlook local freebie want ads, as well as the local classifieds. Farming oriented newsletters or newspapers are excellent sources. The fastest way to sell your hay is at auction. Most farmers' markets and rural produce auctions also auction hay on a regular basis.

Of the above, the horse folks are the best market. Once you've won a customer, they will stay with you. A local boarding stable bought 300 bales from me this year, and ordered 1,000 bales in advance for next year to be delivered straight off the wagon.

Pricing your product will vary from year to year, according to supply. Mixed grass seems to sell the best and usually runs $1.25 to $1.50 a bale in this area. We've had a very dry year, and the same hay is selling for up to $2 a bale and may go higher. Delivery fees work out to about 50 cents a bale. Poor quality hay can be sold as steer feed. The junk hay can be sold as bedding, straw mulch, or composted. We used some for mulch in the vegetable garden, sold some to the mushroom growers, and composted the rest.

Don't overlook "custom" work, making other people's hay for a fee. Some homesteaders grow their own hay for home use and the quantity is insufficient to justify buying their own equipment. This is easier money in that you don't have to sell a product, because you're selling a service. The going rate for this is 50 cents a bale, and the landowner stacks his own.

My first year in the hay business was a real education. I was very fortunate to get hooked up with a custom operator who works in round bales which is a complement to my square bales. I made about all of the mistakes you can make, but I still made enough to pay for the equipment.

Borrowing equipment is not the way to go; it seems that everyone makes hay at the same time. Equipment breakdowns are another fact of life, especially with older equipment. I suggest that you buy equipment based on parts availability, as well as condition and price. A good parts man and a well-stocked local dealer would make a lesser brand machine more attractive, so I hesitate to recommend brands. However, John Deere and New Holland both have an excellent reputation in hay-making equipment. Tractors are an entire story in themselves.

Consider this carefully and well: hay is a lot of hard work in high summer. It is also a good way to make money. Good luck, and I may see you at the auction. ✺

Car repair and crab pots

By Dave Duffy

John Raxa has combined two skills to make a successful living in the small coastal town of Eureka, California. He makes commercial crab pots and repairs cars and trucks.

While earning a degree in automotive technology from the nearby College of the Redwoods, he had worked for six years for a local commercial crab pot maker. Then he went into the crab pot making business for himself for several years, selling as many as 5,000 crab pots a year to commercial fishermen who worked the coasts of California, Oregon, and Washington.

But part of his business involved delivering the heavy iron crab pots to his customers, which meant he had to maintain a flatbed semi-trailer. One year, the repairs to the trailer amounted to nearly $10,000, a sum that took a serious bite out of his income. So he decided to employ his automotive degree and opened an auto repair shop in the same building that housed his crab pot business.

He then hired a mechanic who was glad to have the job, and the mechanic, under Raxa's supervision, not only repaired Raxa's own truck, but was available to repair the cars of customers who needed that service.

Raxa finds the two businesses complement each other. "A mechanic can generally fix more than cars," he said. "I've got a lot of equipment in the crab pot shop that sometimes need repair; he takes care of that too."

Raxa says he gets most of his car business from the local telephone directory, where his ad reads: "HONEST DEPENDABLE REPAIR," and he says he makes himself or his mechanic available 24 hours a day, seven days a week. I'll vouch for that, because that's how I met him. My car had broken down on a Sunday, 12 miles outside of Eureka, while visiting Humboldt State University to watch my daughter, Annie, perform in a chorus performance of the Northern California Honors Chorus. After calling several garages only to find out none were opened, I saw his ad in the phone book and called him.

I had AAA tow my car to his garage, leaving my family behind in the motel. After arriving at his garage, Raxa loaned me his truck so I could go back and pick up my family.

Both Raxa, his mechanic Anthony Scherman, and I suspected the scraping sound coming from my left front wheel was a bad wheel bearing. It turned out to be a small rock that somehow got wedged next to the brake disc.

After removing the rock, Raxa's mechanic asked him what to charge. Raxa replied, "Nothing." I was a bit flabbergasted, because I knew that I had gotten both Raxa and the mechanic out of their homes to work on a Sunday.

So I decided I at least had to buy one of his commercial crab pots, and ask him about his business. It became obvious to me that he was a success because he ran an honest car repair service, just as his telephone directory ad said, and that his crab pots were high quality.

Being a fisherman who has caught his share of crabs, I was impressed by the sturdiness of the pots. They are made of $5/_8$-inch rebar to withstand the abuse of heavy commercial use. He makes two sizes—36 and 38-inch diameter. Each crab pot is wrapped with scrap rubber to help protect it against salt water corrosion. And each contains two metal cylinders which are essential to grounding ocean static electricity to the bottom of the ocean floor so as not to deter crabs from entering. I had not known about the static electricity problem, and the information made the whole car breakdown worthwhile. 🦀

89

"Weekenders' Angels"

By Nanci Vineyard

Like so many of you who also read *Backwoods Home Magazine*, I too once lived in the city and dreamt of getting back to the land. I pursued my dream for many years by lying on the couch, reading magazines, designing log homes in my mind, and wanting to kill the person using a leaf blower across the street. I put on pantihose and mascara, drove on the freeway to a glass building, performed a well-paid but (to me) meaningless task, saved my money, and plotted my escape.

When I purchased a very secluded ten acres in the North Georgia mountains, the pressure was eased somewhat, because at least I had a quiet place to escape to on the weekends. The first and most essential part of my dream had become reality.

After three years of land payments, I had enough equity in the land to swing a construction loan for a house. Despite hardly knowing the difference between a skill saw and an eyebrow pencil, I contracted the house myself. I weathered the alternate urges to commit murder or suicide, the house was finished, the mortgage secured, and I moved.

Although I loved hearing the rain on my tin roof, being able to have chickens, and a huge organic garden, and no longer being constantly assaulted by blaring car alarms, I found that I had a new problem: how to make a living at the end of a dead-end dirt road. I had initially planned on meeting my financial commitments by commuting the two hours back to the city on a part-time consulting basis, and this worked for about a year, until my main client went out of business. I did not want to spend huge amounts of time staying overnight at friends' houses and rummaging up new clients. I desperately wanted to do something closer to home so that I would have the time to enjoy all the reasons I had moved here for.

With my back up against the proverbial first-of-the-month wall, I took a job at the only plant nursery in town, for an inadequate six bucks an hour. But the job barely kept the telephone and electricity turned on. I had to think of something, and fast.

One day while working at the nursery, I noticed a couple who came in and, unlike the locals, did not ask the price of plants. They just picked out whatever they wanted and handed me a VISA Gold card. They were "weekenders," people whose primary residence was in the city an hour and a half down the road, but who had a weekend getaway in the mountains. They started to include a particular flowering shrub in their cartload of purchases one day, but put it back with the comment, "It requires so much watering, and we're only up here once or twice a month." Bingo! I had my idea, and in that instant my business was born. I named it "Weekenders' Angels"—corny but absolutely rememberable.

It has been up and running for two years now, and I am happy to report that while it is not my ultimate, perfect, lifetime solution, it has proved to be a very workable idea for the present. I am paying my bills, providing a much-needed service to my community, meeting some nice folks, and having time to do the things I want to do at home.

The basic idea is quite simple: we perform whatever services out-of-town property owners want done and for whatever reason can't or don't want to do themselves. Our services run the gamut from landscaping, cabin cleaning, storm damage survey, carpentry projects such as adding closets or decks, plumbing and electrical repairs, house painting, and delivering firewood.

The execution of the idea has been like any new business—a couple of years of trial and sometimes error, learning, paying attention to what works and what doesn't, analyzing profits and losses, and making corrections. The underlying key to my success sounds so basic, yet it is so necessary: show up when you say you'll be there, do the work you promised to do, and charge as close as possible to the price you estimated.

I have secured a trademark on my corny name, and have written a procedural manual which includes topics such as how to secure a client base, how to ascertain market rates for various services, how much start-up capital is needed and ways to get it, and how to deal with emergencies and cranky customers. It also includes examples of invoices, response letters, advertisements, accounting records, and what I hope are some beneficial as well as humorous anecdotes. I am marketing the manual, rights to use the name, and my services as a consultant to others who find themselves living in a rural area which has a healthy component of non-resident property owners. While my particular situation involves mountain cabins two hours away from Atlanta, Georgia, the idea could just as easily work for anyone within driving distance of a ski resort area, lake, ocean, you name it, anywhere people have second/vacation homes or weekend getaways. 🖋

Animals and fish

Crayfish farming

By Don and Sharane Wilson

Raising crayfish for food, either as a commercial operation or as a small homestead project, is a country business well worth looking into. It's a well established industry in much of the South. In Louisiana, commercial crayfish farmers raise and sell 85 million pounds yearly. Texas and Mississippi produce similar amounts.

Growing demand

There is a steady growing demand for crayfish, also known as crawfish, on the East Coast. North Carolina, with 14 members in the state crayfish association, produces about 100,000 pounds yearly. The crayfish may be larger and tastier than the Louisiana crayfish even though most large operations raise the same variety—the Red Swamp crayfish (*P.clarkii*).

Farming crayfish for profit is a newly established niche that has growers scrambling for production. The director of Aquaculture for the North Carolina Department of Agriculture (NCDA) says the North Carolina market for crayfish is "strong with definite growth potential," and that they "just need more people producing crayfish."

With over 400 varieties of crayfish in North America alone, there are bound to be dozens of varieties suitable for raising to a large food-size anywhere in the U.S.

In North Carolina, Georgia, and South Carolina the vast majority of crayfish are raised in the Coastal Plain. There are some crayfish farms in the panhandle of Florida. These states are all forming grower's associations to promote both the production and consumption of these tasty

95

crustaceans. Annual crayfish festivals and give-aways happen during the harvest season.

Low investment

Raising crayfish for food and profit is a relatively low investment project, requiring only a moderate amount of labor for a short time period, and it has the potential for a good economic return. "Just about anybody can raise crayfish. The key is maintaining water quality." says NCDA's Tom Ellis. Aubrey Only, and Edenton crayfish farmer for three years, says "Crawfish can diversify an existing farm and add supplemental income."

Need at least one pond

To get started, you need at least one pond with a nearby freshwater source such as a creek, stream, or canal.

Low oxygen content is the main water quality problem. Although crayfish are exceptionally tolerant to low oxygen in their water, they can climb out and walk away from bad water.

Simply running fresh water to the habitat or aerating the water will correct this. If the water is aerated, then the water only needs to be pumped in to replace the pond's evaporation loss. This means the water source need not be very large to maintain the pond, and allowing the water to fall into the pond enough to make bubbles is all the aeration that is needed. A ram pump could be used in some cases to pump water without the need for electricity or gasoline.

The pond only needs to be 1-3 feet deep, and the water need not be crystal clear. Silted or turbid water may even be better, as crayfish don't like bright sunlight and predators would not be able to see them. Crawfish are normally placed in clear water after they are harvested to clear out the digestive system—sometimes called a "mud vein."

Food and growth

The natural food of the crayfish includes both living plant and animal sources—insect larvae, worms, other crustaceans, small fishes, snails, and tadpoles, as well as most dead animal matter.

The bulk of the crayfish diet comes from the high-protein bacteria, fungi, and other microorganisms which cover decomposing plant material. As the plants decompose, carbon changes to nitrogen and becomes more nutritious as well.

The crayfish detects food with its long antennae and the short antennules. It is believed that the sensing of meat juice or blood by the short antennules causes a reflex in the crayfish to turn and move toward the source. Crayfish do not drink; water is absorbed through the gill surfaces.

Crayfish mature in 3 to 12 months. The average life span is 24 months for most species. The Pacific and some American varieties can live 5-6 years. One Mississippi variety lives 6-7 years.

Crayfish possess the power of "Autonomy and Regeneration." That is, they can self-amputate, or drop a leg or have part of one taken by a predator, and grow a new one to replace it. The lost part is fully restored after several molts.

Environment needs

Although varieties of crayfish live within a wide range of environments, they all do best under similar conditions.

The ideal temperature range for rapid growth is 68 to 77 degrees F. Crayfish eggs will hatch in 2-3 weeks at these temperatures. At lower temperatures growth, activity, and egg development slows—and stops completely below 50 degrees F. Above 81 degrees F. most varieties seek shelter and become dormant.

The water must be fresh, with salinity less than 10ppt. Ocean water is about 35ppt.

There must be some calcium in the water (hard water) at between 50-200 ppm ideally. The acidity range is pH 5.8-8.2. Dissolved oxygen should be greater than 3 ppm. Total ammonia should be less than 1 ppm.

Crayfish can tolerate less dissolved oxygen and more ammonia levels, but they respond to these unfavorable conditions by slowing or stopping their molting rate.

When dissolved oxygen in the water falls below 2 ppm most crayfish will climb to the surface for air. They can survive this as long as the gills remain moist (100% humidity), but this is stressful. Crayfish can tolerate lower levels of dissolved oxygen, below 1 ppm, for up to 24 hours if they cannot get to the air.

All crayfishes are more susceptible to environmental extremes right around the time of molting.

Crayfish are very sensitive to synthetic chemicals, especially pesticides and weed killer. Creosote, turpentine, pine oil, nicotine, and pyrethins are toxic to crayfish in very small quantities.

Locating the pond

Choosing the location for raising crayfish is fairly important. The water source can be surface water or a well. A stream can be dammed to form a pond, or small pools can be dug out along the stream. A swampy area or marsh can be dug out or levied. Detailed advice on levee, dam, and pond construction may be obtained from the Soil Conservation Service, county agricultural agents, or local contractors.

In short, nearly any area that can collect and hold clean, fresh water is suitable for growing crayfish. The soil should have some clay to hold the water, and be thick enough that crayfish burrows will not drain the water.

The site should be limed if it is acid. The smaller the area used, the more efficiently it can be managed. Some provision should be made for draining the area, although some species of crayfish do not require an annual dewatering in their life cycle.

Pond construction

Crayfish ponds are generally constructed along the lines of catfish ponds—with a bulldozer—although the water need only be 1-2 feet deep and thus the levee or dam can be lower and less expensive.

The drain pipe should have anti-seep collars to prevent the burrowing of crayfish or rodents that would cause leaks. In order to promote better water circulation, the water input and the drain should be as far apart as possible. In large ponds, "baffle levees" and/or boat trapping lanes can be constructed so as to encourage water circulation. Water pumping, circulation, and flushing is most important in the fall, when vegetation in the pond decomposes and uses up the oxygen in the water.

In a boggy or swampy area that is too soft for a bulldozer, a dragline can be used to build up a levee. The bottom is left undisturbed except for the ditch created by the dragline. This type of pond is generally acidic and may need some lime treatment.

The walls (dikes, dams, levees) have to withstand the pressure of all the water in the pond, and must be watertight. The construction depends on the kind of soil in which the pond is being built.

A soil which is a mixture of clay and sand is best. If pure clay is used, it must be mixed with other soil, as pure clay will crack and leak. Do not use turf, humus, or peaty earth. All stones and pieces of wood or anything that will rot must be removed. These materials will weaken the walls if left there.

Start by placing layers of soil, about 8 inches thick, over the drainage pipes and tamping each layer down until it is compacted. Some people use a large rock or just jump up and down on the soil, but a tamping tool is best. The important thing is to pack the soil down tightly.

The finished height of the wall should be about a foot higher than the water level for small ponds, and about 20 inches for large ponds. The width of the wall at the top should be equal to its height. For a large pond, the wall is never less than 3 feet wide at the top. Most walls are built so two people can walk side by side along the top.

Grass should be planted on the walls to give added strength and prevent erosion. Do not plant trees.

Lime pond bottom

Most pond bottoms will have to be limed before filling. There are four kinds of lime that can be used for this, at the following rates:

Agricultural lime—2021 lbs. per acre
Ground limestone—2508 lbs. per acre
Quicklime—178 lbs. per acre
Hydrated lime—101 lbs. per acre

The lime should remain on the pond bottom 2-3 weeks before filling the pond. This will counteract any acidity in the soil and pond water. Crayfish production can be more than doubled by liming acid soils. The best soil pH is 6.4.

Pond drain

The best type of drain is the double sleeve overflow system. This setup drains stale water from the pond bottom as water is added. The drain pipe goes through the wall or dam and turns up vertically at a "T" fitting inside the pond, to end at the desired water level of the pond. It is screened to prevent escape of the crayfish. A larger diameter pipe is placed over this pipe, above the level of the water, and extending to near the bottom of the pond.

For the complete draining of the pond, the simple Rivaldi valve can be used along with this setup. It consists of flexible pipe, screened, attached to the "T" fitting and kept staked above the water level until draining is desired, then it is allowed to fall to the bottom.

Water requirements

There needs to be some circulation in the water, although if some form of aeration/filtration is used, then only the evaporation loss need be replaced. The inlet and drain pipes should be screened ($\frac{1}{2}$-inch mesh), and be placed as far apart as practical to insure good circulation. Sometimes a screen on the inflow may not be necessary. It is needed mainly to keep out predatory fish. Smaller screen mesh can clog up, so a happy medium may have to be reached in some cases.

The inlet should be above the water level so that it splashes and mixes with air to add oxygen to the water. Both can be accomplished by allowing the input water to cascade over a series of mesh plates or screens on square frames mounted above each other.

Both stream and well water are typically low in dissolved oxygen, and this kind of aeration will overcome these problems. Be sure the water source is free of pesticides and pollution.

Silted or muddy water may have to be run through some kind of gravel-sand filter. This can be a tank or pool where the silt is allowed to settle out before it is drawn off the top into the habitat, or is filtered through gravel at the bottom.

Green, growing water plants add oxygen to the water (photosynthesis), and decaying plant and animal material use up the oxygen (oxidation). The living animals, in this case the crayfish, use up the oxygen to live (respiration). Respiration and oxidation go on day and night, while photosynthesis takes place only during daylight hours. Any stirring or splashing or even wind rippling of the water can add oxygen to the pond water.

The most important aspects of water quality to the crayfish farmer, beside temperature and dissolved oxygen, are alkalinity, pH, and hardness. These three factors are interrelated.

The relationship can be summarized as:

low alkalinity=low pH=low hardness

In ponds, all three can be controlled by adding lime to the water.

Prefer shallow water

Crayfish prefer shallow water, between six inches and one foot deep. For optimum production, no more than 25% of the area should be more than three feet deep. The bottom should be fairly level, with some small elevations, bumps, or ridges. The slightly uneven bottom will give the crayfish more area to burrow. Of course they will thrive on most bottom contours, the main consideration being the form of harvesting planned upon. The smoother bottom allows for using nets or seines.

When using baited traps, just about any bottom conditions will work.

Densely wooded areas will have to be cleared past the shoreline. If the brush is thick, it will make harvesting difficult, crowd out the useful plants, and shade the water, keeping it too cool for optimum production. The excess vegetation will also drop leaves and debris into the water, which decay and use up the oxygen.

The most common pest plants are cattails and water hyacinth. Remove these before they cover the pond, or crayfish production will be greatly reduced. Some good plants for crayfish food and cover are alligator grass and water primrose, as well as pondweed and duckweed. These are normally not discouraged unless they get too thick and hinder harvesting.

Beware of pesticides

Crayfish are extremely sensitive to synthetic chemicals, especially pesticides. Agricultural runoff is very dangerous to a crayfish farming operation. The crayfish can die, or they can accumulate some poisons in their flesh and be hazardous to human health when eaten. Locate as far from farm or pasture land as possible, or try to secure cooperation from the owner to avert contamination of the crayfish habitats.

Stocking

There are usually some naturally occurring local species of crayfish nearly anywhere one would plan on raising them. These are generally the best ones to stock the pond with, as they are already acclimated to the area climate and water. These wild stock can be trapped and placed into the pond as soon as possible. If enough are caught, one would be advised to select only the largest specimens to stock the pond. This will start the process of selective breeding right away—breeding for large size and fastest rate of growth.

One may also attempt to buy the stock from an established crayfish farmer who deals in such things. The stock crayfish should be freshly caught and kept cool and damp until put into the pond. In the south, the usual procedure is to stock ponds with adult crayfish (size—about ¾ to 1 oz.) when prices are low, usually in March. Price may not be a big concern for the smaller operator. Crayfish below ½ inch are very vulnerable to predators. After the first year, the crayfish population becomes self-sustaining. Generally the southern species do best where the pond is drained seasonally. Most northern varieties do not require this.

Jumbo sized

To grow really jumbo crayfish, avoid overcrowding. No more than one adult crayfish per square foot is recommended, with plenty of hiding places provided. Fighting and cannibalism of the newly molted and stunted adult size is the result of overpopulation in a crayfish habitat. More or better food will not correct this, as they are a solitary animal with a strong territorial instinct.

Crayfish growth and survival is best when they have plenty of both animal and vegetable products for food. A good portion of this can be grown or encouraged to grow naturally. Supplementing this with high-protein commercial fish feed or range pellets (cattle feed) produces truly huge crayfish. They cannot easily grow to this size in nature as wild crayfish.

In an aquarium

In my own experience there is some indication that raising crayfish in an aquarium from the very young and newly free-swimming size results in less fighting among them. Raised this way to an inch or so in size gives greater survival rate for stocking a habitat. About 18 juvenile crayfish per square foot of tank is a good recommended density. Trying to raise crayfish to adult size in an aquarium usually results in lots of fighting and competition. It is possible if they are kept separated with a screen or barrier of some kind.

I provide plenty of hiding places for these young, which are barely visible but fully armored minute replicas of adults. Young crayfish

103

molt, or shed their shell, as they grow—sometimes once a month. For about a day the newly molted crayfish is soft and very vulnerable. The others will attack this soft crayfish unless it can hide. I have found that rocks or seashells piled along the rear long side of an aquarium with a gravel bottom makes for an efficient setup, providing plenty of cover with a clear area in front for feeding and observation.

An under-gravel filter or an outside flow-through filter keeps the water clear. Shrimp pellets seem to be the best feed, not fouling the water. Commercial crayfish feed is probably the best food for an outside pond or pool, supplemented with hay.

Raise them as pets too?

The arrangement of rocks allows you to view the crayfish, which are quite interesting creatures. They take an active part in their surroundings, making their own little shelters out of the gravel and rocks, almost like little bulldozers. I even use box turtle shells for the larger crayfish pets, which seem to be the right shape inside. Speaking of pets, pet stores are starting to carry crayfish now, sometimes calling them freshwater lobsters and blue lobsters. I picked up a pair of red ones hoping to get some eggs to hatch from them. Under a grow lamp these creatures glow a bright fluorescent red in strange patterns. Someone was breeding these for pet stores, and also had blue ones available. Seems like a good market niche to me, raising red crayfish to sell for $2 or $3 bucks apiece.

How much can you make?

How much money can you make raising crayfish? It really boils down to how large you grow the crayfish and whether you want to sell them from the trap or process them yourself. You can even set up a soft-shell operation for some real profit (and intensive labor). Full grown crayfish average one to two ounces apiece, and sell for about $2 per pound live and $4 per pound cooked. Soft-shells and tail meat sell for $8 to $10 per pound.

And how much would you like to keep for your own eating, because these crayfish are excellent food, high protein, lowfat, and as tasty as any lobster or shrimp? Try dipping the tail meat in melted garlic butter—you just might want to keep all you can grow. That's pretty much what I do, at least until I can get some more ponds in production.

Don Wilson is author of the 47-page booklet "Small Scale Crayfish Farming," available for $10.95 plus $4.95 S&H from the *Backwoods Home Magazine* bookstore. ❧

Raising fishworms

By Robert Colby

Do you remember the movie "Heroes" starring Henry Winkler? Henry played a Vietnam veteran whose dream was to go to Colorado and start an earthworm farm. His friend, played by Sally Fields, thought he was crazy.

Maybe the idea of having a worm farm seems crazy to you too. But it's not. For one thing, you can make a good living raising earthworms, with annual earnings capable of ranging from $20,000 to $50,000. Another thing to consider is that it's not too difficult. In fact, it's quite easy to get started.

It does take work, just like most legitimate, legal, and honest businesses. However, we're not talking about backbreaking work.

A worm home

To get started you need to prepare a home for your worms. You can start in any kind of container that will hold your bedding material and that will have good drainage. You can use an old washtub, a 55-gallon drum cut in half, or a plant propagation box. These containers are good for starters, but eventually you'll need to graduate to full size pits made of concrete block, brick, cement, or wood. If you've got room you can just skip the smaller containers and build pits from the start. Make sure you put drainage holes in the bottom.

You can make your own propagation boxes, and you should construct them in uniform size so you can stack them. Once you have your propagation boxes, fill them.

For larger scale production you will want to build pits or bins to raise your stock in. Depending on the area of the country you live in, you will build either indoors or outdoors. If you live in a cold region and want to continue production during the winter you should build indoors. If you live in a warmer climate like Florida or where I live—Arizona— you can build your pits outdoors. Once your pits are constructed, fill the bottom with 3 to 4 inches of gravel. Above the gravel put 12 inches of bedding material. An easy starter bedding material is made up of half peat moss and half manure. The manure must be decomposed past the heating stage to prevent burning your starting breeder stock.

Breeder stock

Once the bed is prepared, place your breeder stock on the surface of the bed. You can get breeder stock from an established earthworm farmer or bait shop in your area. There are mail order sources as well. Coverage should be 100 to 200 breeders per square foot. They will quickly burrow down into their new home. Sprinkle down your bedding with water every day or two depending on climate and how quickly your bedding dries. Don't let it get too dry or your worms will die. The idea is to moisten the bedding, not saturate it.

The worms will feed on the bedding for a while so you won't need to feed them at first. After a week or two, put manure on the surface in a ditch down the center of the pit. Do this daily, depending how quickly the manure disappears. Ground grain feeds used sparingly on the surface will help fatten them up for harvest. Water down the surface lightly after spreading a thin layer of grain over it. Spade your bed every 21 to 30 days with a manure fork to loosen your bedding. If you've recently put grain stock on the surface, rake it back to prevent mixing in with the soil. Mixing it in can sour the soil, making it unsuitable for the worms.

Harvesting

You can harvest your first crop in three months if you started your stock with mature breeders. You can tell they're mature enough to breed by the appearance of the clitellum ring around the torso. But if you want any kind of volume to sell you'll probably want to wait a year before you begin sales.

You can keep dividing your stock from one pit into two pits every three months. Every six months you should change your bedding with new compost.

Earthworm soil

Don't throw out the old bedding because it makes great soil for growing your plants or for selling to your local nursery. In fact, if you ask a gardener or nurseryman what the richest potting soil is he will tell you it's earthworm-castings and waste products which add high concentration of nitrogen, phosphates, calcium, and magnesium because they are water soluble and easy for plants to absorb. Earthworms naturally loosen the soil as they move through it, grinding it up in their innards. Nurseries will buy the bedding soil the earthworms have so efficiently and naturally processed. There are millions of gardeners in the U.S. and Canada that are waiting customers.

Selling the worms

For containers to sell your bait worms, use ice cream or cottage cheese cartons from your local dairy farmer. Be sure to poke some holes in the lids with an ice pick so the worms can breath. You'll need a variety of sizes starting at half-pint all the way up to one gallon containers. Check with your local paper company for boxes to ship the containers in when selling by mail order. Use some moist peat moss to pack them in for shipping.

Be sure to squeeze the excess moisture out of the moss. Too much water can cause the worms to literally cook in their containers. To determine what price to use for different sizes of cartons, call some local bait shops to get an idea of what they are charging.

You can market your products to fishermen if you're strategically located near a lake or stream. Gardeners will buy earthworms for soil enrichment. Contact some local nurseries to sell your used bedding. You can also sell worms to other secondary markets like zoos, aquariums, and poultry farms. You can even sell wholesale to other bait retailers.

If you raise earthworms in conjunction with other animals, you help process the animal waste products. Earthworms are a perfect match for raising rabbits. The earthworms feed on the manure and neutralize the odor of rabbit urine. In addition to rabbitries, your customers would also include poultrymen, game bird breeders, fish hatcheries, zoos, aquariums, frog farmers, and laboratories. Zoos and research institutions use the earthworms for food and in soil research, and they are used in aquariums to feed the fish.

In spite of many new competitors in the earthworm raising market each year, there is much more demand than the producers can keep up with. In fact, your competitors may be one of your best friends. Why? Because they are good prospective customers. And in turn you will be a customer of theirs at some point.

When you first start up, you very likely will sell all of your first harvest before your customers stop requesting your product. Your competitors will sell you additional stock wholesale should they have a short term surplus.

Mail order worms

If you want to grow your business you need to do mail order sales. Eighty to ninety percent of all earthworm sales in the U.S. are by mail and the other ten to twenty percent is to local customers.

To advertise, start with one or two outdoor sport magazines. National advertising costs less in proportion to sales than it costs for local ads. National ads save you time, gas, and wear on your car. Run some small test ads in the classifieds in the live bait section. Don't blow your whole ad budget on a huge display ad. Mail order is competitive, but the demand far exceeds the supply in this business.

Selling chickens to an ethnic market

By Dynah Geissal

If you live near an immigrant population, you may have a ready market for products that you already produce on your farm. While most Americans seem to prefer "sanitized," wrapped in plastic supermarket fare, people from less developed countries often have values similar to ours as low impact farmers. If you appreciate different cultures, the rewards of dealing with other groups of people may be greater than merely monetary.

Missoula, Montana has been lucky to be a resettlement area for many nationalities including Hmong (Laotian), Tibetan, and Russian. There is also a university that attracts people from many African and Asian nations.

Many of these people prefer to see animals on the hoof when they buy their food. They like to choose a living animal and slaughter it in their traditional way. That works well for me since the law forbids the sale of home-butchered meat. Pigs, cattle, geese, ducks, chickens, and goats are all candidates for the ethnic market.

I have concentrated my efforts on the sale of chickens, although I occasionally sell other animals also. The Hmong population is my primary customer. That community is large enough that they have been able to maintain many traditions.

The Hmong people are smart, honest, hardworking, and, despite the hardships they have been through, almost always seem upbeat and optimistic. I have really enjoyed getting to know them, although there are some difficulties that you should be aware of if you are considering a similar venture.

An obvious problem is the language barrier, but with patience on both sides this can be overcome. It gets easier as you both learn what to expect, too. The young people learn our language quickly and they can often be counted on to help with the transactions.

A second problem involves the tradition of bargaining that is prevalent in other cultures. In my early dealings with the Hmong I had to face this every time. While I understand that this is a normal part of life for them, I made the decision not to participate. For one thing, they're better at it than I am; but also I'm the only one that knows how much it cost me to raise the animal to the point of sale. I can't bargain for feed or for chickens. My figures are clear and I know what profit margin I need to make the enterprise worthwhile. These are not variables, so for me there is no room for haggling.

A third problem is a combination of the above two—language and the desire to bargain. When the language is new, many sentences come out as a command. It is intimidating at first. An example:

"Old Uncle buys ten red chickens today. He pays $2."

"I only have black chickens today and they are $2.50."

"Old Uncle buys those red chickens."

"Old Uncle needs red chickens today."

This can go on and on. Denying Old Uncle's needs was very hard for me at first. I learned though that this is their way of bargaining exaggerated by a quirk of learning a new language that causes it to be a command instead of a request. Some people are angered or annoyed by this way of talking. Others are talked into selling something that they don't want to sell. To be successful, a person must be firm but cheerful about what they have for sale and what it will cost. I don't have the problem anymore except with an occasional newcomer. One man even teases me by offering a very low price when he comes to buy. Then we both laugh and appreciate the rapport that we have established that even allows for joking.

A fourth problem is that the young people are sensitive about what Americans think of them. Because of that they hesitate to talk about their native celebrations. If a person needs black chickens today, is it for a personal reason such as honoring the birth of a child or is it a community-wide holiday? If they need red today and black next month, what does that mean? How will I know? Even most of the people that I regularly deal with are very difficult to communicate with on this matter. They have had too many bad experiences. Many Americans have laughed at their traditional rites and called them pagan. In fact most Hmong are Christian and want to be accepted as Americans. It has become somewhat easier as trust has developed between us. Still it's a constant struggle to pick up hints about what will be needed three or four months in the future. Hardly ever is it spoken right out.

I enjoy my marketing arrangement with these warm wonderful people. If you think you might enjoy a similar setup, read on and I will tell you what I've learned over the years.

I had never raised large numbers of chickens before. I have 100 layers and in addition I raised 50 butcher chickens every year. Now I raise for sale 100-200 every eight weeks. It's a very different proposition. Starting 50 chicks in your kitchen every spring is one thing. Having chicks in your kitchen all year is not something you would enjoy. Keeping expenses down is primary as is conservation of labor. These are things you don't worry too much about when you raise chickens for the freezer but if it's to be a business you will want everything streamlined.

Unless you live in a very warm climate you will need a brooder house. It should be erected near the house because you will need to check your chicks at least four times a day. A 10x10-foot building will house 100 chicks and 200 if the weather is warm enough for them to run outside.

My brooder house is double-walled with insulation in between. It is good at -20 degrees Fahrenheit unless the wind is blowing from the east, which is where the door is. In those circumstances I have to use a small electric heater if the chicks are very young. Your brooder house should have at least one adjustable vent near the ceiling on a wall not facing the prevailing winds. A window in the south wall will add warmth, light, and ventilation when necessary. It will also serve as an exit for the chicks when they are old enough to go outside.

You will need a hover about 4' x 3' with sockets for two heat lamps. With the two lamps the chicks don't tend to pile up and it also serves as a safety feature in case one lamp burns out. A thermostat is cheap and is a good investment. If you have to be gone early in the morning it is good to know that the lamps will stay on until the house warms up but will go off before your birds are overheated. It is also helpful if the hover can be raised and lowered. Install a light with a switch near the door. You will need it for checking on the chicks and at times you may want to leave it on.

If you can afford it, get commercial feeders and especially waterers. When you're only raising birds for yourself you can improvise but when you're raising them continuously you will want the convenience of having the right equipment. Buying a five gallon waterer was one of the best things I've done for myself. A feeder you can fill just once a day is wonderful too. Then your time can be spent checking on their health and well being instead of on menial tasks repeated several times a day.

You will probably want to try several hatcheries before you find one that's just right for you. Price is important, of course. Most hatcheries have specials that may meet your needs. (Note: Many cultures need certain colors for certain purposes or, more importantly, cannot use certain colors.) All the hatcheries I've used seemed to be reputable but some seem to have chicks with greater livability. That may be genetic but more likely it's how fast the chicks get to you after hatching.

Keep records! Write down every expense beginning with the material for your brooder house. When you have broken even you can celebrate! It's very important to see where your expenses are and how much you make on each chick. Keep a diary. How long did you feed chick starter? When did the birds reach market size? What weight had they attained? To make a decent amount of money on this you have to be really good at it. You won't remember everything, so write it down.

If you encounter disease write down symptoms and what you did about it. Did it work? Almost any disease involving butcher chickens can be prevented. The major causes of disease are not enough warmth, overcrowding, insufficient diet, lack of ventilation, and lack of cleanliness. All are easily correctable.

Setting your price list will be hard at first—another reason records are absolutely necessary. I found that charging by the week works well for me. That way I can make a reasonable profit by comparing how much I am spending on each bird. After the chickens are on whole grain my profit margin increases considerably and the purchaser also gets a better deal with the heavier bird.

My price is much higher than supermarket prices but comparable to those in health food stores. I am as fair in price as I can be and still have it worthwhile for me.

The Hmong people are just one group who appreciate the fruits of a small farmer's labors. There are many other groups that are happy to buy animals that are alive and raised more naturally. If you enjoy people from other places you may find this market a very special one, just as I do.

Note: possible sources for markets are refugee centers, cultural centers, ethnic stores. My experience has been that once you get your first customers, word of mouth will take over. 🙐

Raising goats

By Jayn Steidl Thibodeau

Question: What animal can be used for meat, milk, fiber, brush control, costs a minimal amount both initially and for upkeep, and not only will pay for itself the first year but actually make you a profit?

Answer: The much-maligned goat.

The goat has always been portrayed negatively, whether in Biblical reference or in conversation with the neighbor who chases the kid's pet nanny down the road by your house. In truth, the goat is an intelligent and affectionate animal, which in turn gets it into more trouble than the more easily handled sheep. But while the sheep industry is in a national decline, the profit potential in raising goats on your homestead is unlimited.

Different goats have different purposes. Dairy goats can be used for both meat and milk. A typical Spanish goat, on the other hand, is basically a meat goat that doesn't produce enough milk to make the chore worth your time. The Spanish goat, however, will have an undercoat of hair known as cashmere and can be shorn in the same way that sheep is shorn. The Angora goat is basically a fiber goat, although they have been sold for slaughter.

Using goats in any of these ways can produce a profit over and above the cost of the animal. We have been raising goats profitably for the last seven years, and although we have made every mistake in the book we are still in business, which must say something about just how much profit a goat sideline can give you.

Fencing can be easy

Fencing is the first step to raising goats. If you don't have the proper fencing, you don't have any business with a goat on your homestead. But fencing doesn't need to be expensive. Our fencing originally was free. We used the ever-popular wooden pallets from a lumber company to build a large lot around our barn. They were given to us for the hauling. Later, as we began to show a profit, we added an electric fence.

In training the goats to the electric fence, we discovered that the way to do this was to first put them in a small pen built of wooden pallets with three electrified wires that we ran inside the pallets for an interior fence. After two weeks of this pen, we were able to turn them out in a portable lot with only one electric wire, and they never crossed. Even goats that had been chronic roamers stayed home after this lesson.

Finding goats cheaply

To find the proper goat, you first need to know something about them. If you have a friend or neighbor, go and ask questions. If you don't, go to the local auction house and ask questions there. Find out what terms such as mastitis, foot rot, and smooth-mouthed mean. And touch the goats. Go in with them and feel the udders. A good bag will feel soft and pliable. A bad bag will feel lumpy or hard. You can't always tell by looking, so be sure to touch.

Don't buy anything from the auction at this point; you aren't ready. Auctions are where people go to unload their problem stock, and eventually you will know a good goat from a headache, but you just aren't smart enough at this point.

Ask someone to show you how to tooth a goat, or verify age by the teeth. This is relatively simple, and you must know this to progress to the next step.

Now that you aren't a complete moron about goats, let's go buy some.

While you were at the auction you listened to the market prices, and you know that goats in your area are worth a certain amount. This amount will change from season to season, with fall and winter being the cheapest time to buy goats and spring and summer the best time to sell.

So, listen to your friends and neighbors. Who bought goat kids for their children to raise in the spring, summered them, and doesn't want to bother with them now that the kids are back in school? This is a potential seller. Who didn't bother with fencing, instead staking the goat out all summer? Staking is harder in the winter, so there is another potential seller. Didn't the fellow down the road have three or four goats that have been out on the pavement twice last week? Get down there the next time those goats are out. You'll get them cheap. Watch for newspaper ads. Lots of goats are advertised, and most people don't keep up with the market price.

Some people don't want to spend the effort to winter their goats, but don't want to sell either. Offer to keep their nannies for them in exchange for the kids. Then return the nanny when the kids are weaned at four to six weeks of age. (Or raise them on the bottle.)

If you can't find any using your eyes and ears, all hope is not lost. Head back to the auction, but don't buy the stock yourself. Find a buyer (he'll charge about a dollar a head) and tell him what you want and how much you are willing to pay. Then stay at the auction. Watch your buyer at work. The best buys come at the end of the auction when all the public has gone and just a few buyers are left. Your buyer may buy you a lemon or two; no one is perfect, but his business is to keep his client happy, and he does know goats. And buy several goats. Goats are sociable and easier to handle as a flock rather than singly.

Making money with goats

Now you have your fencing and your goats. The most important thing to remember about making money with goats is that you have to keep them alive. When you bring them in, give them a round of vaccinations that will include tetanus, C&D, and whatever your vet recommends for your area. Don't skimp on the shots, but it is cheaper to give routine vaccinations yourself rather than having the vet do it. Vaccines are available through your vet or through a feed store.

Worm your goat as soon as it comes in, especially if you are in a high-parasite area. Don't overfeed for the first two weeks, which is about how long it takes for the C&D vaccine to be effective.

If you have purchased dairy goats, you have several options open to you. First, naturally, would be dairying. If you don't plan to have facilities to have a Grade A dairy, check with your state health department for regulations. In Arkansas, we are not required to be a Grade A dairy for the first hundred gallons per month. Some states may require a release form.

But dairy milk doesn't have to go for human consumption. You can raise a variety of baby animals on goat milk. Baby calves, lambs, and pigs all thrive on goat milk, and calves and lambs can, with supervision, nurse right on the goat. Or you can buy orphan kids and raise several on each nanny. Some enterprising people have even developed businesses with milk-based products such as soap or casein paints.

The Spanish goat

The Spanish goat has a different purpose. You can't raise orphan animals on her, but she will raise her own kids more easily than the dairy goat can, and she will be much more efficient at converting feed and browse than the dairy goat.

Her main purpose is meat production, so you will look for a nanny who raises heavy, fast-growing kids. Her secondary purpose is brush control. Many people who have trained their goats well lease them out when the kids are weaned to people who need a pasture or lot cleaned out. This saves your pastures if you have an overstock problem, but you need to be sure that you have a clear, written agreement about who pays for your animal if the clients' dog eats your goat. It is best to send a guardian along with the goats if you plan to leave them for an extended period.

The third purpose of a Spanish goat is to produce cashmere. When you select your goats, push back the outer layer of guard hair.

Underneath will be a fuzzy layer, which is cashmere. Your first goats won't produce much, but if you breed for this trait you will have a good crop in a couple of generations. Cashmere sells for a premium price, as not much is produced, and it may sell locally to hand-spinners. Any sheep shearer will shear your goats for a nominal fee.

The Angora goat is going to be targeted to hand-spinners. The kids just don't have a lot of meat on their bones. Don't go with Angoras if your pastures are full of brambles as it will ruin the mohair. And Angoras have been known to get entangled in brush and die before help comes. They are intended for clean areas.

Where to sell goat meat

Well, you could sell your goats at the auction, but if you want to make a little money you will invest some sweat into this enterprise. Goat meat has a ready market as chevon, and it is sold as such to gourmet restaurants and specialty meat shops. Individuals buy goats on the hoof for barbecues, and if you have raised your goat organically you can deal with organic food stores or individuals who will process the goat themselves. You can target a specific market such as an ethnic group.

The point is that there is an unlimited marketing potential out there for goat meat. Publicize the fact that you raise goats by donating a goat for a club barbecue or serving chevon at a church dinner. Once people taste this delicately flavored meat, you won't have to look for your buyers; buyers will come to you. One point, though—if you have targeted an ethnic group as your market, be aware of their special holidays and have goats ready. If you disappoint your customers, it is hard to keep them coming back.

What if my goat dies?

If you lose your goat, find out why it died. You can't learn from your mistakes if you don't know what the mistakes are. Invest the few dollars to have a postmortem done by your vet. You may save the rest of your flock. Also, if you have a goat who dies of natural causes (old age, heart attack, etc.) there are body parts which can salvage the initial cost of the goat. I know this sounds morbid, but it actually can be the difference between losing money and breaking even. Hides can be tanned. Goat skins are a beautiful material and sell well at craft fairs. If the goat had horns, you are in luck. If you will take the time and effort to cure the skull, you have an excellent product which is much in demand for incorporation into the Western decor that is so popular now. I bought an old goat for $25 last year. The goat promptly died, but he was a breed with trophy horns. The skull brought $250. Just remember a piece of advice given to us by a local sage: If you can't afford to lose it, don't buy it.

I hope these tips will be of use to you. We have really enjoyed our goats and the visitors who come to our homestead to talk about or buy our goats. The goat market has been, for us, a satisfying way to make an income from our land without having to go into town and work. With a little luck and a lot of sweat, it can do the same for you. 🙞

Small-scale hog production

By Rev. J.D. Hooker

Usually, when someone forms a mental image of a self-sufficient backwoods lifestyle, the idea of raising a few hogs forms part of the picture. Whether we're thinking about the hill folk of Appalachia, the mountain people of the West, or wherever, slabs of smoked bacon, home-cured hams, buckets of homegrown corn, and leftover slops seem to fit right into the picture.

Ever since the founding of Jamestown and Plymouth, the production of pork, both for good home eating and for marketing or trading purposes, has played a crucial role in the personal independence of many of America's rural people. Hogs possess an amazing ability to thrive under conditions where other livestock could not even survive, and they convert nearly any remotely edible waste into high quality meat. Without hogs, not very many southern folk, white or black, would have managed to survive the incredibly hard, lean years in the battered, beaten, and plundered South following our devastating Civil War. Prior to the enforced death-march of their "Long Walk" to the Oklahoma territory, part of the way in which the Cherokee peoples maintained their independence and increased their wealth was that every household raised at least a small swine herd for home butchering and for market.

Advantages of a small-scale operation

Some of you will have seen the ultra-modern factory-style swine production facilities that turn out several thousands of identical market hogs every year. The idea of attempting to compete with operations of such magnitude may seem impossible. However, you need to

121

understand that the owners of these huge swine operations are virtually slaves to market factors and to their creditors. A single increase in feed costs, a drop in the market price, or a single otherwise-minor disease organism run amuck in their over-crowded pork factories can wipe out several years' worth of profits. The debt load carried by most such operations will often force the owners into bankruptcy after only one such incident, costing them the whole farm.

It's the small-scale pork producer, running between 100 and 500 hogs per year through the market, who might have an unfair advantage. Consider that selling about 110 hogs (no matter what the current price), for a 90%-plus profit will bring you about the same number of spendable dollars as selling 1000 hogs at the more usual 10% profit of the factory hog farm. Keeping a single good boar and five nice-quality sows, raising each litter to an optimum market weight of around 200 pounds per animal, and selling at the average market price will bring you an annual profit in the neighborhood of $13,500. Should the prices fluctuate upwards, you'd make even more income. And even if the market took a 50% nose dive, you'd still be able to realize about $6,750 that year (while a high percentage of factory-style pork producers would go bust). This might be an over-simplification, but you can see how the ultra-low-budget, small-time producer really is the one who has the edge.

Still, while it's potentially lucrative, even such small-scale swine raising isn't something that you'd want to jump into overnight. You'll need to do some homework and preparation before you begin.

Two types of hogs

The first step is to honestly appraise your own temperament and abilities, as well as the physical aspects of your country property. Then decide on the type of hog that you and your property are best fitted to produce. There are many breeds and varieties, and they fall into two major divisions.

First you have the "confinement" type of hogs, like the Duroc,

Hampshire, and Yorkshire, that can do well in crowded conditions. They breed, bear, and fatten nicely while fenced and sheltered in a relatively small area. However, they require daily care, feeding, water, etc. These are possibly the ideal swine for the smaller farm or homestead, not requiring much acreage to bring in a reliable, steady income.

In the other major division are breeds like the Tamworth and Holstein (yes, there are Holstein hogs as well as Holstein cattle). These are capable of producing equally as well as the confinement breeds, while ranging loose in large fenced pastures or woodlots. These breeds require the absolute minimum of care, thriving and fattening quite well on grasses, acorns, roots, and such, which they can forage on their own. They require a much larger homestead acreage for successful production.

None of the confinement breeds do well when attempts are made to raise them under forage-type conditions. Forage-type hogs are equally unsuited for raising under confinement type systems. So this is something that you'll need to decide on before you set up your operation.

Strong and tight

Next you'll need to make a decision regarding what sort of facilities you'll need: shelter, fencing, farrowing huts, etc. This depends a lot on which type of hog you decide to raise. But keep in mind that any structure, for any type of hog, has to be both strong and tight. An adult hog is an immensely powerful animal, easily capable of breaking through poorly maintained fences or collapsing weak housing. And young pigs and shoats seem to delight in squirming out through the smallest break in any fencing or farrowing house. So whether you opt for wire field fencing or some type of wooden fence, and whatever sort of shelter seems right for your situation, make sure that your original installation is both strong and tight, and then make certain that it stays that way.

Feeding

It's in feeding the hogs where you'll find that the smaller producer has the edge over the factory farmer. It's the relatively high cost of commercial feed that forces these pork factories to work on such a high-volume, low-profit margin system. Sure, these high-dollar rations will normally bring their hogs to market weight much faster than less expensive feeds. But due to the feed costs involved, they usually need to produce ten market animals to match the profit realized by lower-volume breeders with a single marketable porker.

Many small-scale producers of forage-type hogs find that moving their herd three times a year works out the best for them. Their hogs spend the spring and early summer on mixed grass pasture; the late summer, fall, and sometimes early winter in the woodlot; and the largest share of the winter in the corn, bean, sorghum, or beet field that was planted for them, and left unharvested.

With our own Spot, Poland China, and Yorkshire confinement hogs, and our small operation, we've come up with a feed system that works great for us. We plant a mixture of corn, beans, and sorghum all together. The entire plants—cornstalks, beanstalks, and all—are harvested for feed. During the summer, we also feed a lot of fresh-mown hay or grass, saving the last cutting for winter hay. Also, every sort of garden waste, potato peels, damaged and spoilt tomatoes, wormy or bad apples, etc., is thrown to the hogs. We also feed them thoroughly cooked fish scraps and butchering wastes. To supplement the feed we produce ourselves, we've also found a bakery outlet store that will sell us a pickup load of stale bread, doughnuts, and other out-dated bakery products once a week or so, for next to nothing. This is a really worthwhile super-inexpensive addition for us, and they are happy to receive even a token payment for this stuff, rather than paying to haul it to the dump.

Such mutually beneficial arrangements are well worth taking the time to find. Other small-scale breeders of confinement-type hogs have found restaurants, doughnut shops, produce wholesalers, supermarkets, farmer's markets, and other businesses whose owners have been happy to save their leftovers, damaged and imperfect produce, etc., for them in return for a token payment. Sometimes establishing such arrangements ends up being the determining factor in deciding the number of hogs your enterprise can support.

Buying your first hogs

As to the animals themselves, once you've determined whether you will be raising confinement- or forage-type swine, you'll need to settle on the particular breed (or breeds) you prefer. There are so many swine breeds (some common, others relatively rare) that this becomes mostly a matter of personal preference. Remember, though, that if there are other swine producers in your area, there will always be some demand for quality breeding stock, so it may be wise to stick with the breeds most popular in your area.

You'll need to select your own original breeding stock as carefully as possible. Check into the records of the producers you purchase your first stock from: litter size and survival rates, early weaning abilities, number of days to marketable weight, feed conversion rates, and related factors are all extremely important. Normally you'll pay quite a bit more for stock with a high production background, but it's well worth the extra cost.

Once our hog shelters, fencing, etc., were ready, and a steady and inexpensive feed supply assured, we were ready to buy our first hogs. Just-weaned shoats (young hogs)—one boar and four or five gilts (young female hogs)—is usually the best option. Starting out with these small, young animals allowed us to become thoroughly familiar with their care while they were still small and easily managed. We also found that by hand-raising our breeding stock like family pets, we ended up with calm, easily managed adult breeders. As we've continued our operation, all of the swine selected as eventual breeding stock has been handled in the same manner.

This is a method which I recommend highly in any sort of livestock raising endeavor. There will always be unexpected developments, whether it's a difficult birth or a thousand-pound boar on the loose.

When these things happen, it's so much simpler and safer to deal with an affectionate beast, rather than an indifferent or belligerent one, that I think it would be foolhardy to use any other method.

Caring for your hogs

You'll need to use wire cutters (diagonal cutters seem to work best) to nip off the razor-sharp needle teeth of newborn piglets, to keep them from injuring their dam while suckling. Sometimes I have tried skipping this step with animals I think I might be keeping for breeders. This is because in our area, we frequently have trouble with feralized dogs attacking livestock. So far, though, I've had pretty poor results, as the mothers usually find those needle teeth too painful. The few successes that I have had, though, have proved that swine with tusks intact can hold off dog attacks.

It's necessary to castrate the young male shoats which you don't intend to keep or sell as breeders. This is a simple, relatively painless procedure, done while the animals are still small. I've found the best tool for this to be a finely-honed sheepsfoot pocketknife blade. I have read directions for attempting this procedure on your own, but I really wouldn't recommend attempting this by yourself on the first try. However, after watching someone else, whether a veterinarian or an experienced hog farmer, cut a couple of shoats, you'll be able to do it yourself.

Hogs also have a few other needs. Chief among these is plenty of water. In fact, fresh drinking water is the most important part of a pig's diet.

They'll also need some way of keeping cool in the summer. Whether that would involve providing some sort of shade, a mud wallow or sprinkler, a creek or ditch flowing through your pasture or woodlot, or some electric fans in the barn, will depend upon your particular circumstances. Too much heat can kill a hog mighty quickly, so you'll need to come up with something.

Winter brings a different set of considerations. Adult hogs that aren't kept in seriously overcrowded conditions can stand an awful lot of severe cold, without any ill effects. But, drafts can kill them off pretty quickly when they sleep. Even forage-type hogs need someplace to curl up out of the wind when they sleep. You'll also find that any sort of hog shelter for winter use must either have a dirt floor, where the animals can scoop out a nice comfy nesting hole, or you'll need to furnish a plentiful supply of straw, sawdust, leaves, or other dry bedding, at all times.

While forage-type sows usually manage to care for their offspring just fine through weaning, you'll normally find that confinement breeds need a little extra care in this regard. That's because the adult sow can handle cold temperatures, but not heat, so she's constantly standing up, moving around, repositioning herself, and flopping back down in order to remain relatively cool and comfortable. However, her offspring need to be kept warm all of the time, and even a minor cooling off can kill them. There is also the constant danger of the sow crushing some of her offspring when she plops back down. There is a simple remedy: just hang an inexpensive heat lamp over one corner of the farrowing pen or hut. This supplies a steady source of warmth for the piglets. The small animals will tend to congregate under this heat lamp whenever they're not busy feeding off the sow, while their dam will avoid the discomfort of this added heat. That avoids the danger of her inadvertently crushing the infants.

Marketing

After a while, you'll learn to judge by eye just when your hogs reach the optimum market weight. After that, your only remaining difficulty is in loading the animals into an enclosed truck or trailer and hauling them to market. I've heard of a whole slew of methods for loading these generally reluctant creatures for hauling, and most of them seem to work well enough. But the only means of loading hogs into my truck that I've found satisfactory involves nothing more than a solid ramp with fenced sides and a good, hard-working dog.

If all of this sounds like a lot of hard work, remember that it's not some sort of easy get-rich-quick scheme, but just one method for independent-minded rural folks to provide themselves with a decent, steady, reliable income. It's not nearly as much hard work as all this might sound like, either, but it does require a steady daily routine of care and maintenance. So why not look into your own circumstances and see if this truly traditional slice of American independence can add to your own situation.

And remember the added bonus of providing your own succulent pork roasts, smoked hams, etc., practically for free as a side benefit of this profitable endeavor. That served as the final determining factor for us, when we first considered raising swine for profit. We feel as if this result alone, even apart from the income we've earned, has been well worth the effort. I strongly recommend small-scale pork production as one of the ideal backwoods enterprises. 🦪

Raising rabbits

By Jayn Steidl Thibodeau

Rabbits. Everyone who has ever tried to raise a garden has cursed them at one time or another. Hunters stalk them in the cool autumn air, hoping to bag enough for a tasty stew. Moviegoers cry over Bambi's friend Thumper, or laugh as Bugs and Elmer Fudd battle in cartoonland. But domestic rabbits could add another dimension to this portrait of rabbits. Domestic rabbits (an entirely different species than the wild rabbit) not only have the capability of producing enough meat from a single pair to feed a family of four for a year, but also can be an economically viable commercial enterprise for your homestead.

Mike and I have raised rabbits for nearly 20 years, and believe me, we have made every mistake in the book —and a few not even listed. But overall, we have learned that rabbits are hardy, inexpensive to purchase and feed, and (providing a few simple rules are followed) not particularly labor-intensive, compared with other livestock.

Shelter

Housing will be the most expensive item in a beginning rabbitry, but used cages are available at reasonable prices in most locales, or it is a simple matter to build your own. Many rabbit raisers utilize an old shed to hang cages. Others simply put the cages under a tree in the great outdoors. We don't recommend the outdoor method because feed-to-weight conversion is better in a controlled environment. Close contact with wood also increases the incidences of an aggravating little critter called the ear mite. If you are using an old shed or a chicken house, be sure the ventilation is adequate and the roof doesn't leak.

Walls and doorways should be secured to keep predators away. The neighbor's cat may look cute lolling about on top of a cage, but when a nervous mother stomps an entire litter to death, the humor in the situation is hard to find.

Having a source of water available is a must. You can utilize automatic waterers instead of using the old crock method, which often leaves the animals without water for extended periods of time. Automatic waterers are very simple to set up using either a pressure reducer or a gravity flow system. Several styles are available. The tube type is great for a warm climate and is really simple to repair. The PVC styles run into a bit more money to set up, but are great for cold weather areas. A heat tape can be run through the lines to prevent water freeze-up. These styles and others are available from dealers of rabbit supplies.

Much of the decision about what breeds to choose will depend on your market. Some people will find that a pet market is what they are most comfortable supplying and will choose to raise a dwarf breed or one of the popular lop or Dutch belt breeds. There are commercial markets that buy pet rabbits for resale to pet stores. The main drawback to this particular operation is that demand is seasonal, peaking at Easter, but rabbits must be bred on a regular schedule year-round. Finding a market for a rabbit that weighs only two or three pounds is difficult, and many breeders resort to the snake food market for disposing of excess stock.

Show rabbits are another "iffy" proposition. Out of a litter of five, there may be only one rabbit that is of show quality. What happens to the excess?

Some breeds, such as the Rex or the Satin, produce gorgeous pelts. If you tan hides well, you may be satisfied with these breeds and find a ready market for your wares at craft fairs.

But if you are interested in a really profitable rabbit, it is best to stick with a white-furred, pink-eyed meat breed such as a New Zealand or a

California. These breeds have been bred for generations to be prolific and for mothering ability and rapid growth. Some other breeds, such as Flemish Giants, have been crossed on the New Zealands and Californias with great results for fryer growth rates, but when kept as does, they are usually too large and eat too much to be cost-efficient.

Colored stock occasionally surfaces in these white breeds, but commercial buyers discriminate in their pricing strategies against the coloreds, so don't save any for your own breeding stock, even if they are pretty.

Marketing

Commercial rabbit processors are located throughout this country, and rabbit is a popular export to Canada. Reports of widespread shortages of rabbit indicate that the market is in a stable cycle, and this is an ideal time to begin a rabbitry. To locate a processor near you, you could check with other rabbit raisers, or purchase a subscription to the magazine published by the American Rabbit Breeders Association (see below). There is a commercial section in the middle of the magazine which lists commercial prospects as well as current market reports.

Rabbit growers are an enterprising group of people, and the majority of rabbits raised in this country do not come from large rabbitries of 1,000 or more does, but rather from small backyard growers of 10 or 12 does.

Those fortunate enough to live near a processing plant may deliver their own rabbits or have a driver with a designated route who will pick up the livestock at a pre-determined spot for delivery to the plant. Some groups of rabbit raisers have even formed informal co-ops with members arranging for large numbers of rabbits to be contracted by the processor and picked up. If you choose this method, be sure your members are reliable; if the contracted number of rabbits is not available on the date specified, it will be difficult to deal with that company again.

Meat rabbits are also a popular item with home marketers. The meat, which is low in cholesterol and tastes somewhat like the white meat of

131

a chicken, is in high demand from certain ethnic groups and is a popular barbecue choice. If you choose to sell your rabbits from home, be sure to sell them live and do any butchering only as a favor to your customer. Accepting money for butchering an animal brings you into USDA and health department jurisdiction, and the facilities required aren't cheap.

Choosing stock

When you pick out your stock, choose does and bucks less than one year of age. If a rabbit is being culled from a rabbitry because it is a bad mother or won't breed, you don't want to blow your hard-earned cash on it. If a doe hasn't bred by one year of age, she probably never will. Likewise, if someone offers you a couple of last year's Easter bunnies who have always lived together, avoid them like the plague. They probably won't breed.

Look for clean forelegs—rabbits clean their noses with their paws and dirty paws indicate illness—and clean anal areas. Hocks (the bottoms of the feet) should be free of sores; thin foot pads that can lead to sore hocks are a genetic trait you don't need passed on. The eyes should never be cloudy or filmy.

Teeth should be short. If an animal has teeth that don't quite meet properly, the result is malocclusion, or buck teeth, which curl around the mouth, making it impossible for the animal to eat. These teeth must be clipped regularly or the rabbit will starve. It is widely believed that this is more often caused by a recessive gene carried by the doe and the buck than by accident or injury, so don't introduce the trait to your rabbitry if you can possibly avoid it.

Check the ears for scaly brown scabs. This is a sign of the ear mite problem we mentioned earlier. If left untreated, it can cause nerve damage (wry neck) and the animal will have to be destroyed. If you do wind up with this problem, a dose of mineral oil or cooking oil will clear up the problem cheaply, or catalogs carry a variety of medications.

Run your hands over the rabbit's body feeling for hidden abscesses.

Prices

Rabbits are cheap in comparison to other livestock for the homestead. Prices vary according to the size and age of the rabbit selected. A good fryer-sized rabbit (41/2 to 61/4 pounds) of about 21/2 to 3 months should run less than $5, while an older doe of 6 months to a year may run as much as $25. If you opt for the higher-priced rabbit, ask to see the breeding records on the parents of that animal. They will give you an indication of how the animal will perform. The lower-priced fryer size won't come with records, as it is probably aimed at the meat market, but for the price, you may want to take a chance and just breed out any defects that appear in subsequent generations.

Some companies advertise the sale of certified or registered rabbits. These can be quite expensive and are certainly not necessary for someone who intends to produce a meat animal. Investigate such companies thoroughly before investing. Most are legitimate, but a few have had complaints.

Because rabbits are so cheap, you may be tempted to over-buy. As with any livestock, get your feet wet before diving in. Rabbits are a seven-day-a-week job, and you may find that they don't fit in with your lifestyle. Ten does and two bucks are an excellent number for a fledgling commercial enterprise. As you grow, you will want to save your own stock from your best animals. It is wise to keep at least one buck for every ten does, with replacements coming up at every stage of growth at all times.

Breeding

Every doe will need her own cage, plus a cage for her fryers after they are weaned. The does are ready to breed at about eight pounds or six months of age (later for the Giant breeds), and at that time you will take her to the buck's cage—never the other way around. Does are territorial and can hurt the buck if they feel threatened in their own territory. You will know that the doe is in season if the vulva is slightly swollen and purplish in color. She should breed within a few minutes. If she doesn't, remove her and try it another day.

The buck should breed her twice, and this will finish him for the day. (This is why two bucks are recommended for ten does.) Don't overwork your buck or you will lower the sperm count, resulting in smaller litters. Mark the date she was bred and which buck is the sire in a book or on a calendar.

Each doe will ideally produce seven or eight bunnies in 30 to 32 days, and you should have a nest box in the cage a few days before. Nest boxes can be made out of scrap lumber. They should be 9 inches wide by 18 inches long and 8 inches tall. We bought old wooden army surplus ammo boxes for about $2 each, and they have worked beautifully. The doe will put some of her fur into the filling material (pine shavings or fine hay) for the babies, which are called kits. The kits will be blind, deaf, and bald when they are born, but they grow quickly and will be out of the nest box in about 2½ weeks. You can breed the mother again at three weeks after delivery, although some commercial rabbitries do it sooner. The kits will be ready to wean at five weeks of age.

Some does will have more kits than they can raise, and other does may only have three or four. Neither is a desirable rabbit, but if you have a doe with too many, just remove a few from her box and give them to the doe who doesn't have enough. Most does will raise just about anyone's kit, no questions asked. Be careful when you stick your hand in the cage, though. Even though you selected calm, sweet-tempered does, maternal instinct is protective, and you may receive a nasty bite for your efforts to help. Wearing gloves might be a good precautionary measure.

Feed

Feed is the most expensive item in a rabbitry, but costs can be cut by getting together with other raisers, contracting for larger amounts at one time, and negotiating for a lower cost. Lots of people try to mix their own feed, but nutritionally, a pre-mixed pellet is best for the rabbit. Most commercial feeds are non-medicated, containing about 17-18%

protein, 17% fiber, and 2.5-3% fat, and the rabbits produce and grow well on these ratios. The most important things to remember about feeding are to find one brand and stick to it, and to remove any moldy feed.

Buying feed in bulk is cheaper, but storing feed for long periods may break down vitamins. Feed should be stored in a dry area, such as a plastic trash can, to prevent water damage. High humidity is also a problem, as the moisture causes the alfalfa meal in the pellets to swell and break apart, allowing mold to form. Moldy feed is a major culprit in rabbit enteritis.

Rabbits have very delicate digestive systems. Because they are so small, any slight diarrhea can kill in a matter of hours. Rabbits are like people when it comes to body condition. Some rabbits will get overly fat on just a little feed, while others are downright scrawny on full feed. A good rule of thumb is to keep your non-lactating does on about four to six ounces per day in the summertime, increasing slightly in the winter, while lactating does and fryers should have all they can eat.

Any change in feed should be introduced gradually. A little hay or alfalfa cubes are a helpful treat for your rabbit, but avoid such rich items as carrots, fresh grasses, or lettuce. Rabbits are best fed at night, because they pass soft feces that are re-ingested, much like a cow chewing a cud. Although they can do this at any time, it is usually a night-time activity and feeding in the evening seems to benefit the animal.

Summer heat is hard on a rabbit; they are more tolerant of colder weather. Older bucks have been known to go sterile in high temperatures, resulting in a lot of money spent on feed and no income from fryers. Keeping back some young replacement stock in January to be ready to breed in the summer months helps. We had one enterprising friend who moved her bucks into an air conditioned room, but she found that rabbit hair kept clogging up the cooling unit.

Cleaning the rabbitry can be a nightmare or a paying proposition, depending on your management. It still amazes me how many of those little round pellets a rabbit can produce, and when there are eight or nine fryers in the cage, the mountain just seems to grow and grow. Fortunately, rabbit manure is a commercial enterprise in itself. Gardeners love it, or it can be the basis for a commercial worm farm.

From our first year, local gardeners would show up at the rabbitry, shovel in hand, offering to clean the place for the manure. We tried this a couple of times, but found that it didn't really work out. The does were upset by strangers banging around in their house, and usually people weren't particularly careful about our equipment or the mess they left behind. A fellow rabbit raiser solved the problem by removing the manure to the back of the building and letting people load up feed sacks at a dollar or two a sack.

Being strapped for time with other livestock to care for, we decided to pursue a different route, and Mike's worm farm was born. The simple addition of a few thousand worms into the manure has kept the build-up under the cages to almost nothing and there is no problem with ammonia or odors. And as an added bonus, he has gardeners and fishermen lining up all spring and summer for the little critters. We still clean out, but only once a year for our own gardening purposes.

Rabbits can be a paying proposition with little more input than an hour or two a day for even a large rabbitry of 50 to 100 does. With proper management, a steady supply of fryers will not only pay the feed bill, but will also produce a regular income and even some excess meat for the freezer.

To appreciate the productivity of rabbits, consider this comparison: A 1,000 pound cow will produce one 500 pound calf per year. In contrast, one doe producing six litters of eight kits can produce 200 to 240 pounds of live weight in a year. So one hundred 10-pound does (that is, 1,000 pounds of rabbits) will produce 24,000 pounds of live weight per year, compared to the cow's 500 pounds.

A wide variety of marketing tactics can be employed with the enterprise, and even the waste products have a commercial value. The disposition of the rabbit is such that young children can help with the rabbit chores, and handling the rabbit requires no expensive equipment, like squeeze chutes or corrals. Literature is widely available, often at a nominal cost. And best of all, although the rabbit is very hardy, if a doe does die, the loss will not put you out of business, as she can be replaced for less than the price of a movie. Is it any wonder that the rabbit is the animal of choice for so many homesteaders across the country?

For more information

Mail-order catalogs carry a variety of rabbit-raising equipment and reading material. Listed below are some of the catalogs we have used or which have come highly recommended by fellow raisers. Prices vary with each catalog, so be sure to comparison shop.

Catalogs:

Bass Equipment Company, P.O. Box 352, Monett, MO 65708. 800-798-0150, (www.bassequipment.com)

Jeffers, P.O. Box 100, Dothan, AL 36302. 800-533-3377, (www.jefferspet.com)

Klubertanz Equipment Co., Inc., 1165 Highway 73, Edgerton, WI 53534. Orders: (800) 237-3899, (www.klubertanz.com)

Morton Jones, 925 Third St., Ramona, CA 92065. 760-789-1544, (www.mortonjones.com)

Safeguard Products, Inc., P.O. Box 8, New Holland, PA 17557. (800) 433-1819. Fax: (717) 355-2505, (www.safeguardproducts.com)

Reading material:

The American Rabbit Breeders Association, Inc. Official Guidebook

Cash Markets for Rabbits, by Jack Messner

Domestic Rabbits Magazine, American Rabbit Breeder's Association, Inc. (www.arba.net)

Domestic Rabbit Guide, an ARBA Publication

How to Start a Commercial Rabbitry, by Paul Mannell

Modern Commercial Rabbit Farming, by Jack Messner
Raising Rabbits the Modern Way, by Robert Bennet
Rabbit Production, by Peter R. Cheeke, Ph.D., Nephi M. Patton, D.V.M., Ph.D., Steven D. Lukefahr, Ph.D., and James I. McNitt, Ph.D.

All of these publications are listed in most of the catalogs we have mentioned here, or you can check with your local library. Excellent information is also available from your local County Extension agent or state university agricultural department, often free of charge. 🦌

Garden and farm

Growing trees

By J.D. Campbell

Young apple trees planted along our pond bank died from flooded conditions when spring rains overfilled the pond and flooded the orchard. Several weeks of continuous rains kept the young trees in a saturated condition and those in the low parts of the orchard did not survive.

Several years later, young peach trees putting on their first good crop dropped the fruit in late spring. There were no peaches. An old and knotted plum tree produced sporadically; some years the harvest was more than we could use even in jams, jellies, and canning the fruit whole, while other years there was hardly a plum.

We learned from our mistakes and soon our trees were bearing year after year. Drainage ditches solved the flooding, and regular applications of fertilizers and sprays solved the fruit drop and feast or famine problems.

A good cash crop

Trees are on the rise as valued cash crops, whether they are planted as fruit-producing trees, Christmas trees, or timber. Even the lowly native persimmon which has long been considered a pest in many areas of the country, springing up like a weed to take over pasture land, is now sought by manufacturers of fine sports equipment.

But they need love

But trees need love. More than that they require constant nurturing just as any other crop grown in a field. That includes spraying, thinning,

141

feeding, and proper pruning. Most farms have an acre or two that can easily be converted into a wood lot or orchard that will not only increase the value of the land, but also provide periodic income for the landowner. Pecans planted along a fence row will become a source of revenue in future years as can pines and firs. Trees nurtured with love can provide a source of retirement income in later years at a time when other sources do not appear as stable.

Most states will help

Most states encourage the planting of trees for windbreaks, erosion control, firewood, fence posts, and for attracting wildlife. Windbreaks serve a dual purpose when planted near farm homes by cutting heating costs in winter and cooling costs in summer.

When planted around fields they protect livestock from summer heat as well as prevent the erosion of valuable soil. Deciduous trees allow winter sunlight through while holding back chilling winds. And many states will even supply the landowner with young trees of various species for planting. Check with your local Soil and Conservation Office as to the availability of free trees in your area. This office will also work with you to plant the trees specific to your needs.

We were fortunate that our 18 acres was mostly wooded when we purchased it. However, it had been timbered twice in as many generations and left so neglected that it now grew mostly second growth pine, cedar, hardwoods, and the paltry honey locust. Through diligent thinning and management it is now a certified tree farm with five acres set aside as wildlife habitat. Early years were spent in hard labor and learning from our mistakes.

The preferred time of year for planting most species of trees is during the late fall and winter rather than spring and summer. This gives the roots, the life support system of the tree, a chance to develop and establish themselves before top growth begins. If the root system is inadequate to supply needed moisture and nutrients to the top growth during dry summer months you run the risk of losing the tree.

Even when a tree has an adequate root system it may need supplemental watering during dry periods. If your area receives less than one inch of rainfall in a week during dry months, young growing trees, particularly fruit trees under two years of age, will require five gallons of water at the roots.

Three keys to survival

The chances of a tree's survival depend on three things. The three most frequent causes of tree loss soon after planting are poor planting techniques, improper preparation of the site, and poor cultivation after planting. If these three are not suitable the chances of the tree's survival decrease considerably. And don't overlook the hazard of browsing animals and rabbits. Precautions should be taken to protect seedlings by fencing, or the placing of individual protective devices around young trunks.

Fence away goats

While establishing our tree farm we had heard about the desirability of goats for clearing a woodlot. Forget it. Goats go for the young tender trees and new growth at the tips of branches. Our goats were fenced away from our trees because they could stand on their hind legs and reach even the most tender branch tips of large trees. All thinning and culling was done the hard way, by hand. Brush was stacked and piled to make habitat for small animals and later nature decomposed the piles so that it went back into the soil.

When an area was hand cleared of brush and open between trees, we planted six-inch seedling. Nearby adult trees also reseeded the area so that today, seven years later, the area is so thickly grown with young timber it needs to be thinned. Thinning provides pulp wood—for making paper, our first cash crop.

Tree farming, however, is more than the planting of seedlings, sitting back for seven to twenty years and then going in for the harvest. Many factors affect the growth of trees and it is imperative to take precautions

143

to obtain maximum growth for the duration of the tree's life cycle: planning, management, hard labor and foresight.

Use superior stock

The selection of superior stock plays an important part in growth and development, and hybridization has developed new variations by producing seedlings with desired qualities of both parents. For example, the crossing of the Jeffrey and Coulter pines has produced an offspring with the weevil resistance of one parent and the rapid growth with less branching tendencies of the other. A cross between the poorly formed jack pine of the Lake States and the lodgepole pine of the Sierra Nevada regions grows faster than either of its parents and is better formed.

What hybridizing means to the landowners is easy to understand when talking dollars and cents, and total amount of wood produced whether it be pulpwood or firewood. Tests have shown hybrids can produce 40 cords of pulpwood per acre in 15 years where the most reaped growing, naturally occurring tree stands require at least 35 years to produce the same amount of wood.

Although hybrids are preferred for rapid growth, good form, and insect resistance, we found the hybrids that we planted were not drought resistant so that many of our young seedlings of less than two years died during an extremely dry year. With the natural seeding of the area and the close planting technique employed, enough trees survived to establish a good stand of pine.

Where irrigation is not possible and rainfall is the only means of watering young trees, and when the farm is situated in an area subject to drought conditions, naturally planted seedlings from native trees may be the answer.

The landowner raising trees must contend with other environmental influences such as air pollution, insects, disease, and fire. Of these, the latter is the more serious threat for it can affect tree growth for many future years. Even where growth does not appear affected, the quality of timber is reduced and also opens avenues for fungus infection. On the other hand, fire may stimulate growth by quickly making available quantities of minerals in ash which would not be otherwise available until after organic matter had decomposed. Many timber raisers rely on fire as a means of eliminating brush which competes for nutrients within the stand.

If you are considering growing trees for whatever reason, learn the general environmental requirements which affect growth and development of the trees you select. And don't regard a single requirement as any more or less necessary than any other. Sufficient sunlight, water, oxygen, nutrients, and seasonal temperatures all play a part in establishing a suitable environment. Check with your local university extension service for tree species and fruit types which do best in your locale.

By knowing existing factors you can produce a favorable environment for tree growth and reproduction. Through irrigation, fertilization, and thinning you make more light available for photosynthesis and more water available for the absorption of minerals. In the case of fruit trees, pruning removes unproductive branches, improves the tree's form, and makes it easier to spray and harvest.

Thinning spurs growth

The thinning of pine stands influences the growth of trees by reducing competition for light above and minerals below. Proper thinning should prevent the suppression of growth. Thinning also tends to increase the size and number of branches, crown, and root system and to taper the trees remaining in the stand.

We thin pines and cedars on our property to a distance of eight feet each way between young trees. This opens the top and allows sunlight to filter through to still younger, smaller trees on the forest floor and also gives enough space for each tree to spread its branches and to grow straight without crowding. For older mature trees, we thin to 12 feet between trees to give additional space. The trees removed during the thinning process are sold as pulpwood. We look for crooked, forked topped trees of about four to eight inches in diameter for this first

145

thinning. By the time the trees are 8 to 12 inches in diameter, about 5 years later, we thin for saw logs.

Near/long term harvests

Depending on the growth potential of the land, the care they are given, and the elimination of unwanted trees that compete for sunlight and nutrients, the big harvest comes 10 to 20 years later. The timber owner can now harvest the biggest trees for logs perhaps 40 to 60 feet long and earn as much as $120 per 1,000 board foot.

Growers of Christmas trees realize a harvest much earlier. Scotch pine is the preferred tree for Christmas trees and they can be grown five to seven feet tall in roughly five to seven years. One acre of land will easily support 1,000 trees to harvest at a cost of about $2 per tree. Christmas trees sell commercially by the foot.

For farmers with little land or land not suitable for cultivation, odd corners, or marginal land tree growing is an alternate choice. Equipment needed is not costly and one can add equipment as the need arises. Start with either a dibble bar or planting hoe, a heavy duty riding lawn mower of no less than 10 horsepower, a three gallon pressure tank for spraying weeds and grass around seedlings to boost their start as well as to control insects, and heavy duty shears for trimming and shaping trees if you are raising Christmas trees or fruit trees.

The most costly equipment is a pickup truck or a utility trailer for hauling seedlings and tools, and as most of us already have one or both of these, the investment is nominal.

Contact your State Forestry Department to see if they furnish trees for your stand or get particulars from the U.S. Department of Agriculture in your state. Obtain all available information on planting, cultivating, thinning, harvesting, and marketing. Start small with no more than 1,000 trees so any mistakes you make will be small ones. Tree farming requires a long range plan but the rewards are well worth the effort and time demanded. ❧

Gathering wild plants and botanicals

By Rev. J.D. Hooker

$\mathcal{M}$any of *Backwoods Home Magazine* readers have already developed at least a minimal level of interest in herbal medicines. Quite a few probably already know how plantain leaves provide ideal anti-infective bandages for minor cuts, scrapes, and abrasions, how jewelweed helps clear up poison ivy, and how dried and powdered yarrow provides an excellent infection-preventing "blood stop powder."

Many also know that by filling a canning jar with fresh mullein flowers, adding as much mineral oil as you can fit, then allowing the mixture to sit for a couple of weeks before straining out the flowers and setting aside the liquid, you can produce the finest obtainable pain-relieving children's ear drops.

Even though you may never have tried this for yourself, it's even possible to tan leather using simple plant products, like sumac galls, oak tree bark, and alfalfa leaves.

So it may not come as a surprise to hear that many of these same wild plants that prove so valuable for everything from curing a headache to preventing malaria are eagerly sought after by cash-paying purchasers. In fact, sometimes it's sort of difficult to even believe the tremendous variety of commonly encountered wild plants and rough weeds that people are actually eager to pay for.

One elderly couple I visit pretty frequently brought in $3,000 of extra income last year, just from collecting sassafras leaves. The U.S demand for the roots and bark of this tree have dropped off lately, but in much of Russia, eastern Europe, and Siberia, the leaves from the sassafras tree are very highly esteemed as a thickening agent for use in stews, gravies, and so forth. This demand drives up the prices that companies here in America are willing to pay for this unremarkable item.

Still, sassafras is only the tip of the iceberg where this couple's "retirement income" is concerned. While I can personally guarantee that neither of them ever works very hard, and only when they feel like doing so (I guess that's what retirement's supposed to be about), simply by knowing where and when to market so many varieties of wild plant products enables them to reap a higher income than many folks get from full-time employment.

While it isn't difficult for someone to learn how to supply themselves with a steady, reliable, and sizable income using these same methods, it's imperative to remember not to get so greedy as to overharvest these wild botanicals. Though many marketable plants are so tremendously abundant that this caution can be disregarded, many others are becoming scarce, even endangered in certain areas, because of over-zealous collecting.

Even here in Indiana, the state has placed open and closed seasons on ginseng collecting because of heavy harvesting pressures. Many other areas have enacted similar rules for the same reasons. Use a little common sense and discrimination and you can supply yourself with a nice part-time income for the rest of your life marketing wild plants. But, if you don't leave some to reproduce, you'll very quickly put yourself completely out of business, and just possibly run afoul of the law as well.

Remember to obtain permission before collecting on private property. Though I've found very few landowners who didn't readily permit this sort of activity, these same folks will usually get downright belligerent over unauthorized trespassing. Just be polite and friendly when you ask, remember to keep gates closed, and so forth, and you should have few problems in this regard.

On most state or federally owned lands, asking for permission to harvest such plants isn't usually required. However, it seems as if on ever-increasing portions of our public domain, removing anything at all is no longer permissible. So, it's best to check ahead of time and learn whether such collecting activities are still permitted on the public land you're interested in.

Equipment

There really isn't much of anything you'll need in the way of equipment. The majority of herb and botanical harvesters never use anything more than a strong stick that's been sharpened to a chisel-like point, along with a gunny sack or two. In most cases, anything more would just be in the way.

In my own gathering endeavors, I almost always tote along a firearm and often a small collapsible spin-fishing outfit. Our portion of the map is well dotted with small lakes and ponds, and the spinning tackle frequently accounts for lunch while I'm out.

The firearm, on the other hand, can usually be counted on for some sort of crop raiding varmint or fresh game on every outing. At times I think that it's really only been the superb accuracy of my "bean field" rifle that's gained me such easy access to so many farmlands in our area. It doesn't matter whether you call them woodchucks, groundhogs, chucks, or whatever, these burrowing animals have cost America's farmers so much in lost crops—as well as cattle, horses, and even dogs with broken legs and other injuries—that once the farmers in your area learn that you happen to be a competent and careful shot willing to eliminate even a few of these grief causing pests, you'll usually find a warm reception almost any place you go.

Of course, the fact that the chuck's hide is worth a little extra money (plus the properly prepared meat being mighty toothsome), makes it easy enough to earn such a welcome.

Identifying plants

Should you have an interest in gathering up some of nature's free dollars for yourself, you'll also be needing some ready means of identifying the plants you'd be seeking after. I've found A.R. Harding's *Ginseng and other Medicinal Plants* and the 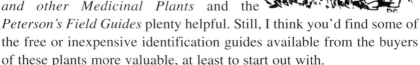 *Peterson's Field Guides* plenty helpful. Still, I think you'd find some of the free or inexpensive identification guides available from the buyers of these plants more valuable, at least to start out with.

Of course, it won't do you much good to gather up even large quantities of the highest dollar roots and herbs until you have a good idea of where you're going to sell them. So I've provided a listing of ready markets at the end of this article. At one time or another I've done business with each of the buyers mentioned and all have proven to be honest, reputable, fair, and even helpful. But you need to realize that each caters to a somewhat different final market, so you'll very frequently find some major differences in what each is willing to pay for any particular item.

Keep in mind, as well, that as these same final markets change and fluctuate, so their purchasing prices can often jump up or down without much warning. I've found it best to stay in contact with each buyer and to stay up to date on current pricings and "wants lists" to ensure receiving the best price for each different item.

Just as long as we'll each harvest nature's bounty in a responsible and respectable manner, there should always be plenty of "free" money growing in our woods and fields just there for the picking.

Markets

Ohio River Ginseng and Fur Inc.
16766 SR 267, East Liverpool, OH 43920, (330) 385-1832
(www.ohioriverginseng.net)
BUYS: raw furs, and some botanicals

Turley's Ginseng and Botanical Co.
1147 Hazel Dell Road, Greenville, IL 62246, (618) 664-2871
BUYS: herbs and botanicals

Mallow Fur Company
601 Asbury Rd., Clarksburg, OH 43115, (614) 495-5681
BUYS: raw furs and ginseng

Mepps (Now Sheldon's)
626 Center St., Dept. 323, Antigo, WI 54409-2496, (715) 623-2382
   (www.mepps.com)
BUYS: squirrel and deer tails, etc.

Hershey's International Inc.
8210 Carlisle Pike, York Springs, PA 17372
   (www.hersheyintl.com)
(717) 528-4495 or 528-8316
BUYS: herbs and botanicals

Hsu's Ginseng Enterprises
T6819 County Road W, Wausau, WI 54402, 800-826-1577
   (www.hsuginseng.com)
BUYS: herbs and botanicals

[Editors note: we found many of these businesses, plus many more all over the country, on HerbWorld's website (www.herbworld.com) in their "green pages." Their address is: P.O. Box 245, Silver Spring, PA 17575, (717) 393-3295.] 🐚

Growing Christmas trees

By Melinda C. Long

$\mathcal{E}$ven when Christmas is a long way off, it's time to start thinking about how to use the season to help you make a living. For some of you, that may mean growing Christmas trees.

In the late 1970s my father, William Hardy, was looking for something to produce for sale on the poor, hilly soil of his farm, so he planted White Pine and Scotch to be sold as Christmas trees. He was surprised and delighted at the demand for them, and for the past three years, his ten acres of trees has shown a steadily increasing profit beginning at $2,000 a year.

Requirements for starting a tree farm

A good thing about growing Christmas trees is that they are not particular about where they grow. They will grow on sandy flats, under power lines, on top of old dumps and in hilly areas. Actually, poor soil suits Christmas tree farming very well. It doesn't produce quite as many weeds and that reduces the risk of seedlings being choked out.

To start a tree farm you need at least an acre. One acre can grow 600-700 trees. Seedlings can be bought from some state nurseries for 10 cents each. Making allowances for some trees that die or are deformed, the profit can be about $5,000 an acre by the time all the trees are harvested.

Your money won't come all in one year because the trees won't mature all at once. A White Pine can be ready for sale in six years, while a Scotch Pine takes longer to grow. And to maintain constant production you must not plant the whole farm the first year. For the first three years, plant only a third each year of the area you plan on tending over-all. Then your supply won't be depleted the first year or two that the trees are ready for sale.

Selecting the right species of tree to grow on your farm will depend on your area. Selecting the right species is important. Plant the most valuable variety your soil will allow to get the highest return on your investment. Planting at least two different varieties offers the customer a choice.

Christmas trees enjoy trends of popularity. Cedars were popular during the 1860s. Douglas Firs and Fraser Firs are preferred today, along with Scotch and White Pine. If you are not sure what variety to choose, get in touch with the District Forester in your area or the Soil Conservation Office. These services, or the County Extension, can also give you the address of a state nursery where seedlings can be bought.

Finally, another essential requirement of the business is patience. It takes an average of seven years to grow a tree to salable age. If you have children, now would be a good time to plant. My father started planting trees when my brother and I were grown. He regrets not having started sooner. But it is not too late for his grandchildren. My twelve-year-old son, Vincent, is already involved and takes pride in instructing his little sister about the trees. There is hard work to the business, but not so much that an older child can't be a big help. Mostly, the work is repetitious. The money earned from Christmas trees can be put towards a child's future. It is a profitable family business that can last into the generations.

Planting

Two-year-old seedlings arrive from the nursery in early spring, and they are planted like most other tree seedlings. The hole must be deep enough so the roots have enough room to run straight down. Cover the stem an inch above the roots with soil. Carry the seedlings in a bucket of water to keep the roots from drying out.

Just like planting a garden, a stake will keep your sights and your rows straight. Don't set trees close to the woods. The shade makes the trees one-sided and difficult to sell. Set trees five feet apart in the row. Leave twelve feet between rows if using farm equipment, such as a tractor and a brush cutter, to mow around the trees. Leave six feet or seven feet between rows if using narrower equipment.

Mowing

Young trees must be protected from being choked out by weeds. This follow-up care is especially crucial in the first year. And two and three-year-olds do better if mowed around more than once. After three years, mowing once a year can be enough.

For a large farm, a brush cutter is necessary. But for an acre, a gas-powered weedeater or heavy duty lawnmower will do to keep weeds down. As the trees mature, early fall is a good time to mow. Not only does it help the trees, but it also clears the way for cutting time.

Trimming

While growing Christmas trees can easily be a part-time job, it is definitely a year around business as each season has its purpose of activity. Early summer brings the important job of trimming. Trimming creates the pyramid shape that Christmas trees are known for. Cutting part of the spring growth causes new buds to appear for the next year's growth, and the trees bush out during the summer.

With a tree pruner, start trimming a tree when it is at least three years old. To begin, select a top branch (there will be several) that is straight and healthy. This is the tree top. Trim it down 8 to 12 inches. It must be trimmed, otherwise it will create a bare gap leaving only a long straight spike. Now going all around the tree, clip at an angle the new growth (called candles) to the shape you want it to be. If a tree hasn't grown much that year, still clip the candle ends. After a tree is three years old, this trimming ritual is repeated every summer.

Cutting, replanting, and drawbacks

When a tree is cut, it is best to cut it even with the ground. This speeds up the root rotting process. After a tree is cut, the soil around the stump seems to be depleted, and a seedling won't grow well in the former tree's shade for at least a year. To give a seedling a year or two head start, plant it between trees that are a couple of years away from sale. By the time the mature trees start to crowd the four-year-old, they will be gone. Insects and disease are generally not much of a problem. Fire can be, and drought will stunt growth. But a real plague to the business is trees that are stolen. You'll always know too, because you have worked the trees long enough to know every one.

Marketing

After nearly a decade of diligence, you may feel a touch of attachment to your trees when cutting time comes. But it's also a proud feeling to know your trees are being enjoyed by others.

One way to market your trees is to invite customers into your field to choose-and-cut their own. This method of marketing is becoming extremely popular. Reminiscent of the days when all trees were cut from free stands, roaming over the fields in search of that special tree is a treat for many people.

My father opened his fields and was surprised by the number of repeat customers and new ones. It was word-of-mouth that brought them. My father has yet to advertise and each year he sells every tree ready for market. Some customers even come as early as October to tag their tree and insure a good choice.

He sells trees at retail price to visiting customers and wholesales the rest to a local grower because he can order fresh trees as he needs them. Before, the trees had to be ordered as early as August and shipped from large farms weeks in advance. Inquiring with local produce and grocery markets may find a wholesale outlet for your trees. And don't overlook non-profit organizations. By offering to help church, scout, or civic organizations raise money, you are also helping yourself.

If you decide to take your trees directly to the customer, a lot near a busy street intersection will give your trees plenty of visibility. A place where people stop such as a busy gas station is also a good location. They stop at your site anyway, and with the holiday spirit drifting freely in the air, what's a few extra minutes to check out your beautiful trees.

Advertising can be worth the small marketing investment, especially if you offer a variety. Dug trees and miniature trees are becoming increasingly popular. Have some burlap on hand for the orders of dug trees. Miniature trees have been popular in Europe for years. They are becoming popular in this country as well. They make fine tabletop trees. Additional Christmas greenery such as Holly and Mistletoe, if it is available, will also add sales. Carrying your customers into the field by tractor or horse drawn wagon to choose-and-cut their own tree adds nostalgic charm. And kids love it.

Prices

In the end, trees are worth what you can get from them. When people see an opportunity they naturally flock to it. Locations around larger cities may be able to charge more, but keeping your prices low will keep the customers coming back for the Christmas break you can give them. Ten or even twenty dollars is a long way off from the $35-$50 trees that some places charge, and your tree will be just as beautiful.

(For additional information on growing Christmas trees, write to the National Christmas Tree Association, www.christmastree.org, email: info@realchristmastree.org, 16020 Swingley Ridge Road, Suite 300, Chesterfield, MO 63077.) 🐾

Raising tobacco

By Rev. J.D. Hooker

Preparing for a crisis involves many things: storable foods, alternative power sources, dependable water supplies, medicines, guns, ammo, and such are readily available—for now—and this particular magazine has printed enough information on living and maintaining a self-sufficient lifestyle that every reader should already know at least the basics about preparing for nearly any crisis.

So probably the next most important thing we need to consider would be how we'd continue to manage should such crisis become an ongoing situation. If the worst happens, what options will we have available when it finally comes time to replenish or replace some vital item or other? Suppose you've just hammered in your very last nail, but the hardware store and lumber yard have both been closed for months. What can you do? What do you possess that someone else would be happy to trade for, and that you can afford to barter away? To put yourself more in demand, what can you have for barter that no one else around you has considered?

One worthy answer that comes to my mind (possibly because of the cloud of rich burley smoke swirling from my pipe as I sit here writing this) is tobacco. Whether the person you're attempting to trade with is actually a nicotine addict or someone raising sheep that have developed a severe worm infestation, a supply of tobacco gives you negotiating power in a barter situation.

Some readers will recall an article I wrote on raising tobacco in Issue #38 (March/April 1996). At that time I was writing about raising tobacco for your personal use. Its many uses include medicinal remedies. Here I'll talk about providing yourself with a substitute for cash in bad times.

One difference I need to point out from the start is that while confirmed pipe smokers, like me, relish the wide range of tastes provided by growing the varieties available from Native Seeds/SEARCH that I mentioned in that earlier article, the vast majority of smokers puff away on cigarettes, not pipes or even cigars, and need a really consistent flavor.

At the same time, when thinking of trade value you'll need to consider quantity and ease of production as well. For this reason I recommend that most folks stick to raising white burley tobacco. This is an easy variety of tobacco to grow and is probably the easiest to cure. It is also open-pollinated, producing capacious quantities of seeds for future plantings.

This past growing season we started some of this seed in one of the manure heated hot-beds I covered in an earlier *Backwoods Home Magazine* issue (Issue #53, Sept/Oct 1998) and some just on window ledges inside of the house, with equally good results. We used empty egg cartons instead of planting flats, filling these with a mixture of roughly equal portions of sand, well rotted compost, and garden soil.

Start with seeds indoors, transition to outdoors.
Plants should be three feet apart in rows four feet apart.

These seeds are very nearly as fine as dust, so I used tweezers to place the seeds just barely under the soil's surface.

About seven or eight weeks prior to your area's final frost date seems to be the ideal time for starting these seeds indoors. Treat them just like you would tomato seedlings (which in fact are a close relative), being sure they remain warm and receive regular waterings and plenty of sunlight. Once outdoor planting time approaches, you need to harden these seedlings off in the same manner as tomato starts, gradually exposing them to lengthening periods of outdoor weather before setting them outdoors in their growing area.

When setting the diminutive little tobacco seedlings into the soil, it seems mighty wasteful of space to set them out three feet apart, in rows four feet apart. But once this variety stretches out and reaches its full height of five to eight feet, with many leaves measuring 18 to 25-inches long, things can start looking pretty crowded even with such liberal plant spacing. Cultivating to control weeds, regular waterings, and weekly feedings of weak manure tea will help this crop produce to its full potential.

Don't bother with clipping off the flowers or the seed-heads as you need to with many other tobacco varieties; you can just let white burley produce all the seed it's capable of. Simply harvest the leaves individually as each one starts to die off and turn yellowish. Actually, in most cases, if you just string the leaves together on a cord (we use braided fishing line) and hang them indoors to dry thoroughly, most smokers will be sufficiently pleased with your product. When dried in an area where it's protected from direct sunlight, this variety ends up with a mild taste that's reminiscent of both cigarette and cigar smoke.

Should you expect your primary trading partners to be cigarette smokers (most likely the case), you'll want to dry most of your tobacco a bit quicker. We found that if you hang up the leaves in the manner just explained, but only until they've turned a nice yellow color, then use heat (an oven or a food dehydrator) to finish drying the leaves out quickly, the taste of the end product was pretty well indistinguishable from commercial cigarettes.

While simply shredding or rubbing these dried leaves to produce a roll-your-own type of tobacco will provide you with a barter staple, most tobacco shops carry simple and inexpensive cigarette rolling machines which turn out a nicely finished product (especially interesting should you happen to be a cigarette smoker yourself). I did a little experimenting this past summer and found that using dried corn shucks, which have been cut to shape with one edge "gummed" using any sort of thick syrup (corn syrup, maple syrup, and simple sugar syrup all worked), along with one of these rolling machines, I could make a perfect substitute for cigarettes rolled with commercially made rolling papers.

Should you have any interest in producing cigars for use as trade goods, a friend of mine who grew up raising tobacco as a cash crop showed me one method for making them and it works quite well.

Once the strung leaves are nearly dried, take them down and sort them, reserving the very best whole leaves for use as wrappers. Allow the wrapper leaves to soak in sugar water, watered down molasses, or some similar weak sweetener, until softened up. While these are soaking, use scissors to cut the other leaves lengthwise into very narrow shreds, discarding the thick center veins. Now use the whole softened leaves like giant sized rolling papers to hold the shredded filler tobacco together like a cigar. Bind each individual cigar tightly with cord until the wrapper has dried out very thoroughly, after which the sugar that's soaked into the wrapper will bind everything together nicely.

Another close friend who chews tobacco found this white burley to be perfectly acceptable after proper preparation. Once the leaves have been strung on a cord and dried completely, he crushes them with his hands and places them inside an airtight container. A ziplock plastic bag works well. Now he'll add just enough molasses, apple cider, heavily sweetened mint tea, or other sweet and flavorful liquid or syrup to moisten the tobacco. After it's been sealed up inside the container for a few more days to absorb the liquid, he says the results are equal to anything he's ever obtained from the store.

For smoking in my old briar pipe, I simply let the leaves dry slowly in a humid spot. Then I just keep them whole and tear enough off of a leaf to stuff my pipe as needed. I'm fairly certain that most other pipe smokers will be equally pleased with this method.

For several years we've also been using tobacco as a reliable livestock wormer. We've experienced good results. For many years tobacco was the only stock wormer available and it worked very well. Feeding goats and other grazing animals about an ounce a month seems to keep them parasite free; stalks, stems, and leftovers all work equally well.

Aside from its value as a vermifuge, tobacco has always had a couple of other important medicinal uses as well. It has been used to treat minor livestock injuries, shaving nicks, or other relatively minor cuts and abrasions. Finely powdered tobacco makes one of the finest styptics or blood stop powders available, stopping minor bleeding immediately while preventing infection. In a similar manner, because of its natural anti-infective properties, we've found that a poultice of dampened tobacco leaves works wonders for cleaning infected wounds on animals. In our nation's early years, tobacco was so highly regarded for

161

these attributes alone that a tobacco pouch was pretty well thought of as a basic first aid kit all by itself.

At present, several commercially available insecticides use tobacco, or one or more of its derivatives, as their active ingredient. Like many other gardeners, we've found that a mild tea steeped from tobacco stems, stalks, and wastes is exceptionally effective for eliminating insect pests from vegetables, bushes, and fruit trees. For our own use we dump about two ounces of tobacco into a 55-gallon plastic drum, fill the drum about two-thirds full with water, and allow this mixture to sit for several days. We then use a pump sprayer to apply this homebrewed insecticide wherever it's needed.

Several other gardening folks we know simply toss all of the cigar and cigarette butts they can collect into a container. They then add water and allow the mixture to set for a day or two before straining out the liquid and applying it in a similar manner. The two methods seem to be equally effective.

By adding about a cup of sifted white wood ashes to a gallon of this insecticide, an effective flea, tick, and lice-killing wash is created for use against those irritating blood sucking pests on dogs and livestock.

Considering how inexpensive the initial cost of white burley seed, along with how easily the tobacco is grown and prepared, and all of the uses for the final product, you can see just how valuable a trading commodity tobacco can be. 🍂

Growing elephant garlic

By Charles O'Sullivan

When a person decides to grow a cash crop, a number of considerations must be a part of the decision.

A product which is inherently pest free not only lends itself to being grown organically but also eliminates the need to buy pesticides. People are naturally attracted to products grown without chemicals. Elephant garlic attracts no pests at all. I have never had a problem with pests eating the bulb in the ground or the vegetation. As a matter of fact, gardeners often plant garlic around the perimeter of their gardens to discourage pests.

High recognition in the market place is a real plus. In other words, it makes little sense to put all the effort into growing a product only to be forced to educate your buyers to the value of your product. The object is to turn the product into money not mini seminars. Elephant garlic is a part of the family of plants which is the third most purchased seasoning in America. Salt is first, pepper is second, and garlic is third. According to the United Nations Food and Agricultural Organization, some five billion pounds are consumed annually around the world.

Competition is a very important consideration. It doesn't make a lot of sense to use your limited space and time to grow a crop which others are also growing in mass quantity. Corn, for example, sells for about 10 cents per ear. If you grow 10,000 stalks and end up with 9,000 ears for sale, at 10 cents a piece, you will earn $900. It sure is hard to get excited about $900. But to the farmer who produces several hundred thousand, the numbers work. Don't compete with large growers!

Elephant garlic solves this problem. In this article you will learn how to turn ¼ acre into a cash flow of as much as $35,000 per year and I'm not kidding!

In America, commercially grown garlic is by far the leader in pounds produced and its production has quadrupled in the last 25 years. California leads all states producing some 90% of all American grown garlic. Garlic production is concentrated in the area of Gilroy, California which is about 70 miles southeast of San Francisco. According to the California Agricultural Statistician, in 1995, 31,000 acres produced 5,115,000 pounds with a value of $179,834,000. Pretty impressive figures but do you want to compete with companies that plant 31,000 acres? I don't.

Commercial garlic, "Silverskin French" and "Serpintine," is different from elephant garlic in a number of ways. One is that it produces multiple bulbs—perfect for the commercial grower who is after large numbers and tons of product. The plant produces fertile seeds which enables

Elephant garlic cloves come in several sizes, (left to right.) A perfect bulb weighs about 8 ounces (center top.) A "giant" clove can weigh 4 ounces, (center bottom.) Grade "A" cloves weight 1¼ oz. and are prime seed stock. Grade "B" cloves are also terrific growers. Grade "C" cloves are sold through retail stores in clamshell containers. (Far right) Hard shell "corms" grow on the outside of the large bulbs and can become a large bulb after two growing seasons.

the grower to sell every last plant. It lends itself to the use of large machinery both for planting and harvesting thereby keeping the cost of labor to a minimum.

Elephant garlic does not produce multiple bulbs. One clove will produce one bulb. Each bulb will consist of four to six cloves, each of which can be replanted. Elephant garlic does not produce fertile seeds. It does produce a center stalk with a rather pretty flower and cluster of seeds but none of the seeds is of any value because they're sterile.

Elephant garlic is almost always planted and harvested by hand. Some growers of elephant garlic harvest with potato pickers but for the most part each plant is removed from the ground one at a time. These factors are not attractive to the large commercial growers in California so they don't grow elephant garlic.

Underproduction is another consideration. There is a reason why elephant garlic retails for $6 per pound while the small, commercially grown, hard-to-peel garlic cloves sell for half that price. Quite simply, there is not enough elephant garlic to go around. It is under produced. When demand exceeds supply, the price goes up. Why is it under produced? To put it in a nutshell, it takes several years for an individual to produce enough seed stock to enable him/her to sell any. (I'll explain that a little later.) We live in an era of instant gratification and most people are not willing to dedicate their time to a project which, although very fruitful, has a reward which is several years away. We want it now!

Elephant garlic can be grown in any climate where a person presently has an outside garden. The person who sold my original seed stock to me lives in Illinois where winters can be rather nasty. He grew elephant garlic quite successfully for many years. I am located in central Florida where it rarely drops below freezing and am having incredible success with the plant. So, I think it is safe to say that if you live anywhere between Illinois and Florida, your climate will work.

Elephant garlic is much smoother tasting than either commercially grown or specialty garlic and, therefore, lends itself to being consumed as a food warmed slightly or as a spice. The cloves are quite large and some can weigh as much as four ounces. I offer these for sale as "Giants." Most cloves weigh between 1 and 2½ ounces. This size should be your primary seed stock. Other cloves are

After eight weeks these garlic plants are well on their way.

somewhat small. I sell them at a discounted price through local health food stores in half-pint clamshell containers. Health food stores love 'em. I have received quite a few sales for large clove seed stock from customers who bought my small cloves locally and wanted to grow their own.

How to get started. Let me preface the following explanation with a couple of thoughts. This is not a phony multi-level marketing scam, nor is it a get rich quick deal that doesn't work. This is honest, hard work for the honest, hard worker producing a real product with real value. Depending on the amount of money you have to purchase seed stock, this project will take you from three to five years before you can sell anything. So, if you are not the type of person who can dedicate him/herself to a long term project, don't even start.

I am in my fourth year growing elephant garlic and expect to clear $35,000 selling product this year. Last year, I cleared about $8,500 and bought enough new seed stock to completely fill my area measuring 110' by 137'. I have 27 three foot rows each of which has about 4,000 plants growing. I started out with less than $200 invested.

Let's say a person started with 100 cloves. Each clove will grow for

166

8 to 10 months (depending on the length of your winter.) It will then split into four to six cloves each of which is a genetic duplication of the mother and can be replanted. The 100 cloves will have become 500. Don't sell any. Replant for a second season and the 500 cloves will become 500 bulbs each of which will have four to six cloves. You now own 2,500 cloves. Don't sell any. Repeat the process for a third year and you will possess 2,500 bulbs (12,500 cloves) and now you can start to sell. As long as you retain your seed stock of 2,500 cloves, you can sell 10,000 cloves and never go out of business. I sell my large cloves for 50 to 60 cents each. With this as a guideline, your 10,000 cloves are worth about $5,500. If you want to become a larger grower, put off selling for one more year and you will have in excess of $25,000 worth of elephant garlic available for sale. But it will take you four years. If you have more money to invest in seed stock, you can cut the number of years down. By starting with 500 cloves, you will save one year. ❧

Soybeans

By Jill Fox

Need a cash crop to take up the slack between harvests of later crops? Try edamame, the green, edible soybean.

You've heard of using soybeans to make tofu, soymeal, and soyburgers, but did you know there is a variety that is picked green to be eaten fresh—and fetches a good price in the right market? The Japanese call it edamame.

These soybeans are a main summer snack in Japan, where you can find them even in pubs, and are enjoyed with beer the way we would use peanuts. If you try them, you'll know why. They have a delicious, smooth, buttery taste, with just enough crunch. And you don't have to worry about it being unhealthy. We've all heard of the nutritional value of soybeans.

Preparation couldn't be easier: boil them in the pod for about three minutes, put them in a bowl, and shell as needed. I like mine with a little salt.

But why bother growing them to sell? Well, they can bring around $2 a pound or more.

They are grown the same way conventional soybeans are grown, but their growing range extends further north into the cooler climates.

To use wasted space, I grew my soybeans between the strawberry rows, in four rows about 50 feet long. We harvested several bushels (a bushel yields about 50 pounds) in spite of the rabbits, which seemed to be the only battle in this enterprise.

Soybeans are easy to pick—even the children can help. You can expect to harvest them late in August, but you must have perfect timing. You'll want to pick them just as the green pods fill out, but before they turn yellow. I made the mistake of waiting a little too late with some of mine and had to reduce the price at the market.

I weighed them, packaged them in zip-lock bags, one pound each, and took them to a local Asian food store. I had talked to the owner of the food store previously to see if they would be interested in selling my product before I grew the soybeans, so I already knew I had a market. Check out your nearest Asian food store and see what the frozen soybeans are selling for. Then charge a little more than that for your fresh ones. The patrons were happy to get this fresh treat, since previously they could only buy frozen edamame.

This is a specialty crop, but with a little marketing ingenuity, you could sell this to gourmet restaurants, or set up a booth at the farmers' market offering free samples to give people a taste of their subtle but addicting flavor. You might just create your own market for edamame.

You can buy these soybean seeds from Johnny's Selected Seeds, (www.johnnyseeds.com) 955 Benton Ave., Winslow, ME 04901, 877-564-6697.

Johnny's sells several varieties, with different harvest times. These soybeans are genetically different from field soybeans, but you can use the latter in the same way. They just won't be as "buttery." 🐚

Providing services

Nursing ~
a perfect backwoods career

By John McLane, RN

For many of us, a job in the traditional economy is crucial to being able to maintain our chosen lifestyle. Others who are pondering a move out of the cities are hampered by economic concerns. Yet a rural lifestyle should be about practicality, flexibility, and pleasure taken in the work we choose. When approached properly, a nursing career can provide all of this and more.

To most Americans nurses are creatures that exist in hospitals and doctors' offices, or take care of those in assisted living facilities or nursing homes. While it is true that the majority of those working in the field are found in these establishments, and thus are concentrated in the larger towns and cities, a nurse can find work nearly anywhere, particularly in this time of massive nursing shortages.

As demand increases for the small pool of practicing nurses, prospective employees are finding higher wages and greater flexibility in scheduling are par for the course. Once you have your certification, you can create your own position to a degree rarely found in the service sector, and you can do so while practicing skills that are immensely useful to yourself, your loved ones, and your entire community.

Education and types of nurses

Each state has its own Board of Nursing which sets the exact policies for local education and licensing. While most states do not recognize each other's nursing licenses yet (we are working on this as we speak), a degree or diploma from an accredited nursing school is accepted anywhere in the country. Generally, there are two levels of nursing licensure, the Licensed Practical Nurse (LPN) or Licensed Vocational Nurse (LVN), and the Registered Nurse (RN).

The LPN/LVN licensure usually requires about a year of course work, with these programs frequently offered through junior colleges, community colleges, or vocational schools. This level of nurse is frequently employed in large facilities such as hospitals and nursing homes, though they may also be found in small doctors' offices or in some home health situations. The LPN/LVN is a skilled provider, but has limits placed on their scope of practice (many states, for example, limit medication administration by these nurses) and thus generally commands a lower salary than the RN. Nonetheless, LVN/LPNs are in demand, and many nurses are either content to practice at this level or use it as a launching pad to RN licensure.

The RN is what is most commonly thought of when people speak of nurses. Traditionally, many RNs were trained in programs run by hospitals, these being three years in length and known as diploma programs. Diploma programs have been largely replaced with college-based schools of nursing which offer either a two-year Associates Degree (ADN) or a four-year Bachelor's Degree (usually BS or BSN). Both types of degree enable students to take the licensure exam known as the National Council Licensure Examination (NCLEX). Upon passing this exam, students are able to obtain a license to practice as an RN.

The difference between ADN and BSN is much smaller than that between LPN/LVN and RN. Both ADN and BSN students receive the RN license, and pay scales are generally very close if not the same. A BSN is generally required for jobs focused upon independent action, such as Public Health Nurses or administration.

Nursing programs have spread across the country as demand has grown, and are increasingly found in rural areas. "Satellite Programs" attached to major nursing schools are frequently offered through rural college campuses or small local hospitals. Many programs exist that allow a nursing student to complete most coursework via the Internet, with the hands-on training taking place at the nearest hospital. With this spread of programs has come a focus upon making them practical for adults, so many schools allow part-time attendance or offer night classes. Your local community college and/or hospital will have much more information.

Areas of practice

This is where nursing becomes particularly attractive to those looking to work part-time or in rural locations. Most nurses still work at hospitals or large care facilities, but even the smallest hospitals generally offer flexible schedules to attract nurses. If you do not need benefits, nearly all hospitals will take you on with a 10-20 percent bonus to your pay as a per diem nurse. Per diem nurses can design a schedule with the needs of themselves and the hospital in mind, and choose not to work at all during other times, such as harvest or during family-focused periods. Even if benefits such as insurance are needed, many facilities will work very hard to keep staff through flexible scheduling. While you will need to adhere to your workplace's staffing pattern (8 or 12 hour shifts, shift turnover times), you can influence strongly the days, shifts, and amount you work. An additional percentage will be added to your pay if you work evening or night shifts. Hospitals and nursing care facilities understand the nursing shortage, and should treat you like the commodity you are.

If your area has no hospital or nursing homes nearby, never fear. The range of alternative jobs is great. Schools frequently need a part-time nurse for the students, and local knowledge is always a plus. Local doctors will need help in their offices. Home care services provide nursing care to patients who need it but can not stay in the hospital indefinitely. These services offer perhaps the greatest flexibility, with you choosing your patient load and arranging visit times around your schedule.

Local and state governments employ rural Public Health Nurses who

175

help educate, track, and treat disease, and serve as local resources to the community. Many businesses employ nurses to treat their staff. Insurance companies use nurses to review cases, often at home over the Internet. Government programs present in rural areas such as WIC and Worker's Compensation often hire nurses.

With another couple of years of education leading to a Nurse Practitioner or Nurse Midwife degree, you can establish your own practice in some states. Best of all, all of these roles put you in direct contact with your neighbors and community in a role that is appreciated and admired.

Nursing school is a large investment of time and money (though grants and scholarships abound), but the return is immense. Nursing teaches you skills that you will use to others' benefits for as long as you live,

For more information about becoming a nurse:

American Nurses Association:
8515 Georgia Ave.
Silver Spring, MD 20910-3492
http://nursingworld.org/

A directory of nursing schools:
All Star Directories, Inc.
2200 Alaskan Way
Seattle, WA 98121
http://www.allnursingschools.com/

National Student Nurses
   Association:
45 Main Street, Suite 606
Brooklyn, NY 11201
718-210-0705
http://www.nsna.org/

Nurseweek (free nursing
   magazine):
800-770-0866
http://www.nurse.com/

National League for Nursing
61 Broadway
New York, NY 10006
800-669-1656
http://www.nln.org/

and that will make you a valuable, contributing member of your family, church, community, and nation. Nursing allows for good pay and flexibility within your job, and a great sense of job security. After all, no matter how bad or good things get, people will always need help and people will always need nurses. 🍂

Be a clown

By Cynthia Andal

Would you like to make a bit (or a lot) of extra money while working flexible hours? Would you like to make more than $20 per hour? This sounds fantastic, but I did it by becoming a clown in a small town (pop. 6,000). This is the ideal home business if you love children and like to have fun.

What you need to start

You should be able to outfit yourself completely for under $100. The actual cost depends on the prices in your area and how much you are willing to scrounge.

Supplies

Oil-based makeup, brushes, and baby powder for your face: You can buy these at theatrical supply stores. Be sure the paint for your face is oil. Anything else will flake and look horrible. Buy at least three colors of paint and a separate brush for each color— small for your eyes and medium for your cheeks, lips, and nose. You'll need one large powder brush for taking off excess baby powder. Medical adhesive or a special nose adhesive and colorful sparkles make a great nose, but if you opt for the traditional red honker, these are available at theatrical supply stores. Baby oil will take your make-up off gently when you're done.

A wig: These are available from the theatrical supply stores as well. A funny hat completes the head look. If you go to the local thrift shop, the possibilities are endless.

177

A costume: Look in the thrift shops for wild ties, huge shoes, and colorful shirts. Add pockets, patches, tassels, or anything else that looks clowny. If you're really creative, sew yourself a costume.

Water-based face paint: This is for painting children's faces. Be absolutely certain it comes off with water or you're likely to have some irate parents! These paints come in a few forms, and it seems the easiest ones to use are the pencil-shaped ones. Try to buy a package with lots of colors.

Balloons! Check the yellow pages for a balloon dealer, and be sure to get good quality balloons specifically for animal tying. For these you  will also need a hand pump. Qualatex™ (www.qualatex.com) puts out a beginner's package with 144 balloons, a hand pump, and a complete animal tying booklet. It will show you plenty of animals to get you started on your way.

You may want to pick up a few extras like a squirting flower or an oogah horn. Later on you can tackle the unicycle riding.

What you'll need to learn

Now that you've got everything, practice a bit for your kids, husband, dog, or goats. Get a good repertoire of balloon animals to tie and faces to paint. Be sure you know what the childrens' current heroes look like because you're sure to get a lot of requests for them. You may want to take the time to learn a bit of simple magic or juggling or even a whole lot of elephant jokes. The local library can help with all of these things.

Now that you're a clown

Next, learn to paint your own face. The library will have some excellent books to help you decide which look you wish to achieve. It takes a little while to get a steady hand, so be patient. Lightly pat baby powder over freshly painted face parts. This soaks up the extra oil in the makeup so that it won't smudge. You could be a happy or sad clown, or add freckles or eyelashes. The limit is your imagination. Remember to go over everything with baby powder liberally.

If you decide on a paint-and-sparkle nose, paint a triangle in the color of your choice on the tip of your nose. Paint over this with spirit gum and quickly dip your nose in the sparkles. Do not go over this with baby powder.

Now…you're a clown! Put on your wig, hat, and costume and act clowny. Be silly for a while. Choose a funny, appropriate stage name. Anything memorable like Sunshine or Rainbow works well.

It's time now to get customers. Once you do a few jobs well, word of mouth will bring you more customers than you need. One week I did a job for the daughter of the grocery store manager, and the next week I got a call to do a huge family Christmas party for 30 children. Put up a sign that says you're available for children's parties in the post office or any other community bulletin board. Advertise at the florist and in the paper, and your phone will be ringing off the hook.

What to charge

Do not undersell yourself. Most entertainers (magicians, jugglers, comedians, etc.) charge about $40 per hour. I charge $20 for 10 or fewer children. I always stay for at least one hour, even if there are only five children there. If there are more than 10 children, I charge my base $20 plus $2 extra for each child over 10. For the really large parties, like company parties, we agree on special prices depending on time, age, and the number of children involved. Check your competitors, if there are any, to see what they're charging and price yourself accordingly. You may find other opportunities arise, like balloon deliveries or wedding decorating. You will need more equipment and financial outlay for these, but it could become a stable, profitable, and fun income.

Once you learn the ropes and gain confidence, this job could be both enjoyable and rewarding. ❧

House cleaning

By Steven Gregersen

How would you like to make more money per hour than you employer? It's not only possible, it's routine. At least it's routine if you work is house cleaning.

For the last five years my wife has been cleaning up (in more way than one). She's been cleaning other people's houses and offices and making pretty fair return on her labor.

Like most families today, we found ourselves in a perpetual budget balancing act. When our children were small it was babysitting that brought in the extra bucks. But, babysitting has its bad points and after your own children become "potty-wise" the thought of changing another dirty diaper becomes even less appealing. Sure she could have gotten a part-time job somewhere but who wants to work for minimum wage? When a job cleaning the local doctor's office became available she called to check it out. That job led to another, and then another, until she was turning down work.

Then, as now, she has found house cleaning to be a pretty solid way to set her own schedule, enjoy the benefits of a home business, and provide a steady source of income.

As the owner of her business, she controls the number of hour worked by the amount she takes on and controls her schedule by the type of work she accepts.

Housecleaning is an occupation that's likely to expand in the years to come. As more women enter the work force there will be a greater demand for someone to do the housework that neither spouse may then have time to do. Let's face it, after fighting rush hour traffic and listening to employers, customers, and children complain, who has the energy to do housework? Paying someone to clean the house is an investment necessary to ward off insanity. And many clients will pay more per hour than they make themselves.

If you can work without supervision and don't mind a job that's physically tiring but financially and spiritually rewarding (the people who hire you, unlike husbands and children, value the job you do and will show their appreciation), then you might want to consider cleaning up at house cleaning. After all, isn't it time you began getting paid for work you've probably been doing (until now) for free?

How much can you make?

There are two methods used to set the rates you charge. Both have good and bad aspects.

The first is to charge a straight hourly fee. This means you agree to work for a set number of hours at a per-hour rate.

This is more flexible for both you and your employer. It allows time for the unusual jobs that may be outside of your normal schedule. If your client wants you to leave the normal duties and spruce up a spare room, for instance, it's no big deal. There's no temptation to rush through the house (and risk breaking things) when you work by the hour. One thing to watch for, however, is the temptation to "drag your feet" instead of doing your very best.

Some people will not contract for your services unless it is by the hour. They've probably been "burnt" by previous house cleaners who charged a per-room fee and did sloppy work.

The second option is to price your work on a per-room basis. Fees are set for a bathroom, kitchen, bedroom, etc. and the amount of work done in each room is standardized. If, for instance, in the bedroom, you agree to vacuum the floor, change the bedding, and dust, be sure your client understands that taking down the curtains for cleaning or window washing is not included in the base price. The expectations of both the

181

client and you should be clearly understood or there will be trouble later.

This method of pricing is appropriate if you expect to hire others to work for you. It does provide incentive to work faster (and make more money), but be careful, it's also easy to become careless and break things because of the emphasis on speed.

Ultimately the quality of your work will not vary with either pricing method. If you are a conscientious worker you will do a good job; if you're dishonest or sloppy your work will reflect it.

Set your prices to be competitive with local market conditions. Get some estimates for your own house from your competition and set your own rates near theirs. In the city we now live in hourly rates are in the $7 per hour range. [(Editor's Note: At the original printing of this article this figure was accurate, now nearly 20 years later average rates for housekeeping are $12-20 per hour, depending on location.]

The type of work you do is up to you. You may limit yourself to house cleaning only or you may include laundry or other work as you desire. The business is yours to do with as you please. It is best to let prospective clients know of limits you've set before you make a commitment.

Hours/finding work

You can set your hours by the type of work you accept. If you decide to work in the evenings, your best prospects will be businesses that are closed in the evening or night. My wife's first client was our local doctor. She cleaned his office and examining rooms two evenings per week. If you clean homes instead of businesses, you will probably work during the day while the residents are at their jobs.

One of the main advantages of the house cleaning business is the flexibility you will have in setting your own hours.

If you are new to an area, take out a classified advertisement in the local paper. My wife began like this in our present location. She made contact with two customers by this method.

She also answered two advertisements from people who needed a house cleaner. One of these people told her friends and three more clients were obtained this way. (This takes the turn of a soap opera now when two of her clients were married. She now remains working for them and the others.) She has limited herself to these five, working 35 hours per week total. This allows her to work extra hours occasionally if someone has something special scheduled and needs extra house cleaning done in preparation for the event.

Expenses/Uncle Sam

Like any business you must allow for expenses when you set your prices.

Equipment can be elaborate or you may want to use your household appliances. In many cases, you can use the equipment and supplies owned by the homeowner you're working for. If you expand and hire employees you'll eventually need industrial grade apparatus. In the beginning it's better to rent what you don't have for those heavy duty jobs. Don't forget to include such expenses in your pricing structure.

Advertising is a business expense you may need to allow for. Usually once is enough unless you expand your business and begin hiring employees.

If you live in an area where litigation is a popular form of problem solving, you should consider buying liability insurance. My wife is rather selective in whom she cleans for and we've decided not to buy insurance. You must make your own decision about this matter.

If you plan on taking a vacation, be sure to add this expense to your pricing structure. You'll need to make enough during the year to finance your time off and you will need to plan for someone to do your work while you're gone. Most private homes will just do without you but most businesses will expect someone to clean while you're on vacation.

As a self-employed person you will be responsible for the full percentage of Social Security taxes and the normal overload of state and federal income taxes. Depending on your income you may need to pay an estimated quarterly tax payment to the IRS. The best advice I can

183

give you is to find an accountant and follow directions.

There have been two articles in *Backwoods Home Magazine* that should be read. See "Taxes—a good reason for you to start your own small business", and "A crash course in small business record keeping," both available in *Backwoods Home Magazine: The Best of the First Two Years.*

House cleaning is an occupation that will allow you to set your own hours and pay. It can be tailored to meet the special needs of the single mother who needs a flexible schedule, the student who wants part-time work, the person who wants a business they can start with a small cash outlay and expand as needed, or anyone else who desires flexibility and independence in their occupation. 🙠

Teaching skills

By Sherry Wietelman

People have been passing skills to the next generation since the beginning of civilization. In ancient times, skilled craftsmen trained young apprentices who became skilled craftsmen and trained their young apprentices. Apprenticeship was the accepted method of teaching others a skill for thousands of years.

Now, more than ever, there is a need for teaching others how-to skills. As office workers lose their positions because of downsizing in large corporations, they find that they have no skills to support themselves and their families. Adults needing training or retraining have created opportunities for skilled craftspeople and artisans to develop and teach adult education classes. Those people who have skills can share their expertise with others and get paid for it at the same time.

When many of us inventory our skills, we sell ourselves short by thinking we don't know anything that anyone else would want to learn. Many people are surprised at what other people will pay to learn. Cabinetmaking, fence-building, sewing, jelly-making, converting to wind or solar power, home maintenance, organic gardening, starting a compost heap, furniture construction or refinishing, and simple auto maintenance are just a few of the many possibilities for adult classes. And college degrees aren't a necessary teaching credential, because it's your experience and basic know-how that people want.

Whether your motivation is financing an independent lifestyle or passing down skills from one generation to the next, teaching others what you know can be satisfying and fulfilling. But before you decide to teach a class, there are five steps you need to learn in order to make your classes the best they can be.

Choosing a subject

The first step to take toward teaching an adult class is to analyze what you can and want to teach. The best teachers are those who enjoy what they're doing and want to share their knowledge and skills with others. You must also analyze your possible audience and think about locations where you can hold your class. Community centers, churches, and continuing education programs at community colleges are all possibilities. You will need an appropriate and safe place to teach your class.

Planning a curriculum

Once you've decided on what to teach, you'll need to decide how much to teach, or the scope of the class. You can't possibly teach your students everything you know, so you have to decide just how much information is necessary for them to become competent at the tasks they are learning. If you're teaching students how to change the oil in their cars, they don't need to know how the engine works or the history of cars in America. They need to know where the oil plug is, how to take it off and put it back on safely, and how to put more oil in. Giving your students too much information will frustrate and confuse them. But remember—the safety of your students is your responsibility. You will need to teach them any safety rules first.

When you've decided what your audience needs to know, you'll need to break it down into small chunks. Just as you learned to walk before running, your students will need to learn certain information before other information. Arranging the small chunks of information and simple tasks in the proper order is called sequencing. Sequencing the information will help students connect the chunks of information more easily and quickly.

Preparing lessons

Once you have decided what to teach, how much of it to teach, and the order to teach it in, you will be ready to prepare for your first class. You must answer questions such as, "What will I do the first class meeting?" Preparing a written outline will ensure that you cover everything you need to cover the first class meeting. Your students will also need to know whether you will provide the tools, equipment, and/or supplies that they need or whether they should bring their own. Handouts for your students, such as a class syllabus or agenda, written objectives for students to meet during the class, and procedure sheets for students to refer to while practicing skills, are other items you will need to think about and possibly prepare.

Don't overlook the Consumer Information Catalog (www.pueblo.gov) as a source of free or low-priced materials for your class. Universities engaged in research and County Extensions are other sources of low-cost information. They often produce fact sheets which are generally inexpensive and provide the most current information available. Oklahoma State University and the Oklahoma County Extension Service in Stillwater, Oklahoma, publish an extensive collection of fact sheets on agricultural, environmental, and home economics topics.

You can also check in the government documents area at large public and university libraries for information published by the federal government. Other good sources are trade and professional organizations, which publish current literature on the occupation or interest they represent. Whatever your source of information, make sure the information you give your students is the most current available.

Facilitating learning

If you've done your homework up to this point, you should now be prepared to instruct your students. When you are giving students background information, it is helpful if you try to relate it to something they already know. Explaining why the information is important will also help them better understand and retain the information. However, for the hands-on skills, you will need to demonstrate correct procedures and allow each student plenty of time to practice afterwards. As an example, say you are teaching a bicycle maintenance class. When instructing students about fixing a flat tire, you'll need to demonstrate the procedure, then allow each student to fix a flat. Circulate while they are working and correct any mistakes you see by reteaching the part they didn't get.

Evaluating results

As a teacher, you will want to continually evaluate your students. There are two types of evaluation. The first type, formative evaluation, occurs when you are circulating and watching the students fix their flat tires. You are evaluating how well they understood your demonstration of the procedure. The second type, summative evaluation, occurs at the end of a block of instruction. It can be a written exam or a hands-on performance check that looks at both procedure and product.

The product in the flat tire example would be the repaired tire. The criteria you would use to evaluate the tire might be that it must hold 30 pounds of air for a minimum of three hours. Summative evaluation gives you a picture of how much information and skills your students have learned, and more importantly, how well you have taught them. Keep in mind that adult students aren't necessarily interested in receiving a grade, but they are interested in succeeding.

Teaching others what you know can be fulfilling and rewarding. Nothing feels quite as good as seeing one of your students succeed in learning a new skill. Whether you've organized a class for profit or taught your grandchildren how to churn butter, you've made a positive impact on another person. And if you've done it right, you've made new friends for the rest of your life. 🌢

Selling sandwiches

By Donn Rochlin

There's a saying in Sedona: "The surest way to make a million dollars in Sedona is to move there with a million dollars." Well according to my experience that turned out to be true with money in general, but the decision to move to the beautiful and seductive red rocks of Sedona, Arizona, turned out to be one of the greatest experiences of my life.

Not knowing quite what to expect in making the transition from the "hubbub" of Fresno, California, and having been born and raised in Los Angeles, I was about to embark on an entirely new and challenging life change. Imagine, a town with only one stop light, one movie theater, two markets, and a main street you could hear a pin drop on after 9 p.m.

Even in the light of this major downsizing now going on in my life, I remember thinking, "With my background in sales and marketing it shouldn't be any problem to get a well paying job."

Well, rude awakening #1: No jobs. With no savings or finances to fall back on, the financial realities of living in a small town started to set in. After months of scraping up odd jobs (hodding bricks, singing telegrams, landscape helper, housecleaning, and even washing dishes), I had had it.

I remember laying in my bed staring at the ceiling and thinking, "There's got to be something I can do to show this town and myself, I'm here to stay. I'm not going to be one of the financial casualties forced to abandon my dream of living where I want."

Interestingly enough, it happened to be the day after Thanksgiving and I started to think about all that leftover turkey and how for weeks after the feast my family would live on it—turkey soup, turkey sand-wiches, etc.

I started reminiscing back to years ago, in Los Angeles, when my wife came up with a great idea to deliver snacks to employees who worked the graveyard shift at several of the convalescent hospitals in our area. Having once worked at one of them, she knew that it was difficult for them to find any place to eat at that hour of the morning. She prepared some sandwiches and various snacks and hit the streets. Even though it provided a little extra income, the business was short lived, as she got weary of getting up at midnight every night.

So here it is, at least six years later, and as I'm laying there a light goes on: "That's it! I'll start a lunch delivery service."

I jumped out of bed and called a friend of mine who I thought of because of her culinary talents. I told her about my idea. The next morning we appraised the leftover turkey and agreed we could get 12 to 15 sandwiches out of it. I said "Let's do it. You make 'em and I'll sell 'em."

When I arrived at her apartment the next morning, I was amazed. She had worked her magic. I mean these where the most beautiful sand-wiches in the world, three inches high with crispy lettuce, bright red fresh tomatoes, mayonnaise and spices, and everything a turkey sand-wich is about. We decided to charge $3.75. "People will go crazy," I predicted.

I loaded the beauties into my cooler and headed out into the winter frost at 9 a.m. I walked into any business showing signs of life and announced myself.

"Hi. I'm the Sandwichman. We're a new lunch delivery service in town. Would you like to be included on our daily route?"

From that day on, I rarely heard a no. I returned three hours later with nothing more than crumbs in my cooler.

Needless to say it was the beginning of a lot of fun, a profitable busi-ness, and a genuine service to the community. Each day we'd add a few more sandwiches to the cooler.

About four weeks into our enterprise, and with steady growth on the horizon, we decided we'd better get legal. We were definitely going to outgrow our apartment kitchen, not to mention the attention we'd soon draw from the health department.

Before securing the necessary permits we would need an approved commercial kitchen. It needed to be something affordable and available to us every morning at 5 a.m. I came up with the idea of contacting the local Elks Lodge. They only used their kitchen for special events and never early in the morning. It was perfect.

We struck a deal with them and set up production. With our permits in order, we now qualified to purchase all of our supplies through a wholesale food distributor. I remember how excited I was to watch those sandwiches run down our assembly line, each one being christened with the "Sandwichman" label and popped into the cooler.

Soon, we had hired our first employee to help build sandwiches, and within a couple of months we had to hire three more salesmen. Our route had grown more than five times. We were really on the map now.

We expanded our menu to include not only turkey but tuna, chicken salad, pastrami, and seafood burritos. One of our most requested items was our homemade fudge brownies. In the summer months we offered salads and fruit kabobs.

We became so well known I remember people coming up to me in the parking lot on my day off, "Hey, Sandwichman, can I get a sandwich?"

So, in less than six months with the help of some good friends, a good product, the support of our community, and the desire to live in one of the most beautiful parts of the world, we were a success.

Even though we moved on to fulfill other dreams, I always look back on those two years as a reminder to go for the dream to live the way I want. I think it always gets back to a basic principle I learned years ago: No matter where you are, find out what people want, give it to them at a fair price, and count your blessings. 🎵

Start a post-construction cleaning business

By Dorothy Ainsworth

Wherever construction is going on, there will be a big mess left in its wake that somebody has to clean up. That somebody can be you, and you can make excellent money doing it. Cleaning only one sizable house a week can gross you $2,000 per month.

If you're the energetic type, in good physical shape, and a fussbudget about detail work, you're "da man" (or woman) for the job. You should be comfortable with ladders and heights, be willing to work long hours on short notice, and maintain a positive attitude and cheerful disposition. But most importantly, you must be dependable, even if you're a grouch.

Contractors are almost always in a pinch to meet deadlines (open-house showings, escrow-closings, etc.) and will be calling you at the last minute to clean a house. You'll have two or three days max to complete the job, no matter how large the place, and with subcontractors still underfoot making messes. (That's where the cheerful disposition comes in.)

To build a great reputation, you have to just do it, no whining allowed. You and you alone will be responsible for making the house presentable to sell, or if it's presold, making it turn-key ready for the new owner to move in—maybe Martha Stewart herself. It has to sparkle.

Getting started

Check out some good books at the library on cleaning, and read up.

192

The experts have a lot to offer in tips and advice that will help you look and feel like a pro, even on your first job.

Think up an original name for your business. Beware of borrowing anyone else's idea. You will need a name (DBA—"doing business as") to apply for licenses.

The next step is to get licensed, bonded, and insured. This is the part none of us likes, but there's no way out unless you want to risk a fine if you get caught. (The contractor who hires you can also be fined.)

A city license is nominal (under $100 most places). Here in Oregon you also have to have a contractor's license to do post-construction cleaning. This requires renting and watching a set of videotapes, available from your local contractor's board. The nine-tape program addresses the legal aspects of the business, not the technicalities of building. You then take a multiple-choice test and when you pass you are issued your contractor's license number, which you will use on your business cards and advertising.

The cost here in Jackson Co., Oregon is about $250. Call the Construction Contractor's Board (CCB) under state listings in your phone book for specific info in your area. (Regulations are always changing.) The CCB will send you an application

A lot of work, but well worth it

193

packet. Simply follow the steps. They want your business.

Bonding and insurance for one year is about $500 (or less) depending on the amount of coverage you need (accident & liability) and is available either through the CCB or privately. They have a chart to determine your needs. Look under "Business Insurance" in the phone book and call around for the best rates.

This may all sound complicated, but it isn't. Just pick up the phone and get started. Professional people are exceedingly helpful. They will guide you through the process; they do paper work for a living. All you have to do is sign on the dotted line and give them a check. There's no mystery involved.

Now it's time to sit down with your "partner-in-grime" (if you have one) and dream up a business logo for your business cards and ads. Keep it simple; keep it cheap. It can be a simple sketch of a squeegee or broom. You don't have to hire a graphic artist unless you have money to spare. Print shops, like "Kinkos", have catalogs of sample illustrations you can pick from and lettering styles to choose from. They'll even help you design your card.

While you're at it, have them print up some flyers announcing that you are ready for business. Then look through the Yellow Pages under "Contractors" and send a flyer to each one. It'll add up to spending about 50¢ (envelope, stamp, flyer) per potential $500 client. It's well worth the effort and expense.

You can also go around to construction sites, introduce yourself to the general contractors, and personally hand them a flyer and a business card. This, along with a handshake, is great PR, especially if you have a Jim Carey or Julia Roberts smile. Keep in mind that they will be taking a chance on you the first time around, so you might offer "satisfaction guaranteed" or something to instill their confidence in you. No good businessman likes to take a giant leap of faith without some convincing.

Equipment and supplies

You're almost ready to start swabbing the decks—but you need a mop! Actually you need a lot of things, starting with a pickup truck or van or any vehicle that can carry a ladder. (I wouldn't recommend a motorcycle, although that might be a cute logo.) If you spent all your cash getting licensed, go down to the hardware store or janitorial supply house, open an account, and yell: "Charge!" like Teddy Roosevelt. Or use a credit card. Or borrow money from the proverbial "brother-in-law." With the profit from your first two jobs, you'll be able to pay off all your equipment and supplies. The rest of the year will be gravy.

Bare-bones list of materials:
- 30-foot extension ladder, installed with a leg-leveler kit for uneven terrain (very important for safety)
- 6 to 8-foot step ladder
- 3 to 4-foot step ladder
- small or medium Shop-Vac (wet/dry type) for window tracks and heating ducts
- regular vacuum cleaner (upright or canister) with long hose attachment for stairs
- window cleaning tools (buy quality and cry only once). Note: You can buy the specialized window tools you need from a janitorial supply, or order them from a catalog. (There is a huge list of supply houses on the Internet.)
- tool belt for window tools
- mop and mop bucket
- broom and dustpan
- plastic putty knife scrapers (1½-inch size is handy)
- toothbrushes
- bamboo skewer sticks (for tight corners)
- lots of soft cotton rags (Wal-Mart sells 18 washcloths for $5)
- rubber gloves (surgical-type is best)
- big soft-bristle scrub brush for showers and tubs

195

- quality spray bottle (again, buy the best)
- gallon of non-toxic cleaning solution (like "Simple Green")
- assorted cleaners for label removal, etc. ("Goof-Off", acetone, or non-toxic citrus cleaners)
- plastic buckets (Two medium-sized will get you started.)

The total of the above list is about $850. Now you're ready to roll.

The bid and the contract

Here in southern Oregon the going rate for post-construction cleaning is from 18¢ to 20¢ a square foot (referring to living space, not the garage). The higher end of the range is based on difficulty in cleaning, such as huge high picture windows, hard to reach skylights, the number of windows, complicated fenestration, extensive high ladder work (steep hillsides, etc.), and other architectural details that require extraordinary work.

In addition to the rate based on square footage alone, you may charge extra for anything that is unusually time consuming, beyond the normal procedures, such as excessive glue on floor seams, paint overspray on window frames and trim, etc.

To simplify the paper work, your contract and bid can all be on one page, with a provision stating that when the bid is actually signed by both parties, it then becomes binding.

If you are a glutton for punishment you may offer to clean up the outside premises too, which may include dump runs. There is always a lot of scrap lumber to be salvaged if you want it for your wood stove or whatever. When in doubt, ask, but the contractor probably won't care; he just wants the place cleaned up.

The time to secure this extra work is when you make your initial contact with the head honcho. Ask to be called well in advance of the interior cleaning job, to do the exterior job. Before you write up your bid, also ask if he (or she) wants the garage floor included in the estimate. (The garage windows are automatically included.)

Window cleaning technique

Perfectly cleaned windows are a priority for a successful business. You will be a great asset to the contractor if you can do it all when you give him a bid. It simplifies his life and saves him time and money not to have to call in another specialist. Contractors love that. The following advice is from a professional window cleaner. This same guy informed me that it's a misnomer to use the term window "washing" in the industry. He said if you want to get really pretentious you might call yourself a "vertical-silicon-surface engineer" who specializes in architectural fenestration. Back to reality. To avoid liability, examine all windows carefully in advance and report any scratches to the general contractor. Almost without exception window glass comes from the factory with a few blemishes, scratches, or anomalies—some even between the panes. They must be noted ahead of time. It will be hard to go back later and say "I didn't do it!" His furrowed brow and red face will reveal his skepticism. Proper blade technique must be emphasized because if you scratch a window it will have to be replaced. Even label removal can be risky with improper razoring. You and your reputation are at stake here. Practice on your own windows first. Cleaning windows is an acquired skill that requires enough practice to make it look like an art. Needless to say, do not use an inexperienced worker to help with the windows.

The procedure:

1. Spray labels liberally with window-cleaning solution to soak and loosen them. Spray the tracks at the same time and let them soak while you're doing the window.

2. With a new razor, remove labels and other debris by using the scraper in one direction only. Dragging a razor backwards does not remove anything, but it can trap grit under the blade and scratch the window.

3. Spray the window again, wash it with a special window mop, then squeegee down or across in broad overlapping strokes, blotting the

197

squeegee edge on a lint-free rag occasionally as needed.

4. Upon close inspection of your handiwork when finished, if you find any stubborn specks the squeegee didn't get, scrub them off with #0000 steel wool. (Only use the finest gauge.) Spray and squeegee again if necessary.

5. Wipe tracks until perfectly clean. Use a toothbrush and/or skewer stick to get into the corners. (Note: Cleaning the tracks can sometimes be the most time-consuming job in the house.)

There are several techniques and tricks-of-the-trade used by professionals. This article just scratches the surface—no pun intended.

Standard house-cleaning procedure

1. Don your rubber gloves, but carry a dust mask and ear plugs with you.

2. Remove all window labels.

3. Vacuum window tracks.

4. Clean window tracks first, or as you clean the windows.

5. Clean windows inside and out, wiping errant drips off the tracks, frames, and sills as you go.

6. Vacuum all cupboards and drawers in the entire house. Remove bottom drawers and vacuum beneath. There will be sawdust in every corner; be methodical so you don't miss any.

7. With a bucket of cleaning solution and lots of soft clean rags, wipe, wipe, wipe every surface of every cupboard, drawer, closet shelf, bookshelf, door, baseboard, and windowsill in the house. Be sure to get the tops of doors, the molding, and trim throughout the house. Again, be methodical so no surface is skipped. Rinse rags often so you're not just spreading dust around to dry into fine powder. (Remember, Martha Stewart may be checking it with her white glove.)

8. Clean showers, tubs, basins, and toilets with a soft scrub brush and cleaning solution. If label removal is a problem, use acetone (first choice) and a plastic putty knife. For very stubborn label adhesive residue, you may have to experiment with "Goof-Off," lacquer thinner,

methyl alcohol, or as a last resort, toluol (a serious solvent). Rinse all porcelain surfaces and polish them with a soft dry cotton towel. Polish all chrome fixtures until gleaming. Clean mirrors with your special window solution and squeegee. (Use this opportunity to look in the mirror and comb your hair; you're probably a mess by now.)

9. Mop bathroom floors and dry with a towel to a lustrous sheen, whether tile or linoleum.

10. Wipe and polish kitchen and utility room appliances and all counter tops. Use stainless-steel-spray-cleaner on stainless. Ammonia products (like "Windex") streak stainless steel and are a definite no-no on marble. Always read labels when in doubt. Scrub and polish the kitchen sink and fixtures.

11. Vacuum out all heating/cooling ducts by snaking the vacuum hose far down the ducts to suck up all the debris you can reach. This job is very important because when the system is turned on it can spew clouds of fine Sheetrock dust all over the house. (And smoke will come out of the contractor's ears.)

12. Vacuum all carpet in the entire house, using the hose attachment along wall edges and baseboard ledges.

13. Wipe tops of all electrical outlet covers. Micro-dust settles on everything. This special attention to detail will not go unnoticed by Martha's eagle eye.

14. Gently wipe chandeliers and light fixtures, or dust them with a lambswool duster. Vacuum the insides of sconce-type lights.

15. Clean all thresholds.

16. Damp-mop the kitchen floor. If the kitchen and dining area is hardwood, save this job for last, and mop as you back out of the room so the floor will remain unscuffed. Use a few drops of lemon oil in the mop water and wring the mop almost dry. This trick-of-the-trade leaves the floor with a flawless sheen.

17. Sweep and/or vacuum the garage if it was included in your estimate. Wipe off the water heater and any other dusty surfaces.

18. As a finishing touch (like Tinkerbell and her wand), leave a little vase filled with a bouquet of flowers (supermarket price) on the kitchen counter with your business card and a congratulatory note, along with a "Thank you for your business." This gesture is well worth the $10 for the goodwill it spreads around. You'll soon earn a reputation for being the best, and you'll have all the referrals you can handle, including repeat business for maintaining clean windows for the new homeowners.

Hiring help

If you need to hire help I recommend you do it through a temporary-labor service agency. You pay the agency directly for the hours an employee works and they act as a surrogate employer, handling the payroll for you (federal and state taxes, insurance, workman's comp.). Of course they charge a fee and a one-time security deposit, but it's worth it.

When you are first starting out it's the easiest route to go because it's responsibility-free for you. The agency will even provide you with the manpower you need, satisfaction guaranteed. (If you aren't happy with who they send out, they'll immediately send a replacement.)

If you choose to pick your own help, they require your prospective employees to register with them in advance and possibly be screened with a drug test and background check (which is understandable since they are insuring them).

The agency issues you a timecard to fill out and send in upon completion of the job. Then they promptly send the employee a paycheck and bill you at the same time. At the end of the year they issue W-2s and spare you that grief too.

On average you can expect to pay from $8 to $12 an hour for help. After a trial period, if an employee proves to be an excellent worker, it would be wise to give him or her a raise. Good help is such an asset to your business and so hard to find, that it's just common sense to pay people what they're worth and keep their morale high.

Keep in mind you'll have to train your employees on-the-job to do the work exactly the way you want it done—fast and efficient as well as methodical and meticulous. You can't just turn 'em loose on the house and expect a miracle. It's imperative to type up a checklist so nothing gets overlooked. After the first house you'll know how long each chore should take, so make a note of that on your list also. From experience I've found that the average 2,000 sq. ft. house takes a minimum of 20 hours to complete.

Someday, when your business grows to the point that you have crews of employees, you may want to incorporate and become the big-shot employer yourself. At that juncture you can drive around from site to site overseeing the worker bees, take coffee breaks, and hire a book-keeper and an accountant. But for now your partnership with a friend or your husband-and-wife team, or just little ol' you working your glutes off, is the starting point. If you are a conscientious person and a hard worker, there is no doubt you'll make it in this business. ❧

Substitute teaching

By Don Fallick

$\mathcal{I}$ have a regular job that's not as regular as I would like, so I fill in by working part-time as a substitute teacher. I work only the days I want, six hours a day. The work is not strenuous and pays $55-$150 per day, even here in low paying Utah. If you like kids, easy work, and a flexible schedule too, read on.

Requirements

Requirements for substitute teachers are easy to meet, but vary from state to state. Most states require at least some college, often a year or less. In Utah you must be 21 years old and have at least one year of college to be employed by a school district as a substitute teacher. But there are ways to get around this requirement. If you are employed by an individual school, all you need here is a high school diploma. To find out if you meet minimum requirements, call your local school or school district. Laws vary so much that there is no other way to tell.

Most districts require you to be 18 years old (21 in some states), and to have a clean police record, especially concerning child abuse. Every district I've ever applied to has required a fingerprint check by the FBI. I don't consider this too intrusive. I wouldn't want my kids supervised by a known child molester, either. If you can't pass such a check, please don't apply.

Surprisingly, your education need not relate to the subjects you want to teach. I studied English in college, but have successfully taught many other subjects. Nearly always, the teacher provides something for the students to do that doesn't require your expertise. Your main job is to take roll and enforce discipline. Glorified babysitting, really, but it pays much better than "real" babysitting.

You'll need to apply for the job a few weeks before the regular school term begins. You may have to attend a "training" session, but don't expect to learn anything about substitute teaching. Training covers pay schedules, parking regulations, and other employment practices. You'll receive an employee handbook and a map of the district. The "nuts and bolts" of substitute teaching you learn on your own or from other subs. Take heart! After a day or two you'll feel like an old pro.

Elementary/Secondary

Schools are divided into two categories—elementary and secondary. Elementary includes Kindergarten through sixth grade. Some Kindergarten teachers only have one session and only get half a day's wages. Grades one through six are usually six-hour "full day" jobs. You will generally teach the same class all day long, but the day will be broken up into "subject" periods: math, reading, etc. You will sometimes have recess duty on the playground. Discipline can be a problem in elementary schools, especially with fourth through sixth graders, and especially in bad weather. But it's usually not as bad as junior high school. Many subs love teaching elementary school, but admit it's harder work than teaching secondary.

Most secondary school teachers have to teach several different subjects. This goes double for substitutes! While the sub office will try to offer you classes you know something about, the real reason they ask for your preferred fields is to find out if you have any unique qualifications. For example, I happen to speak French fairly well. Since I'm the only sub in the district who does, any time there's a call for a French teacher, I get called. My experience writing for *Backwoods Home Magazine* has also helped me get journalism classes. So be sure to list your qualifications for any class you want even if they are not "official."

In general, you'll find that required classes are the least fun to teach, while "electives" are the most fun. The difference is in the students' attitude. Required classes have lots of discipline problems; electives have few. Beware, though: some classes that are called electives really are not. For example, most junior high students are required to take either Choir, Band, or Art. They have a choice, but are not really free. These classes have some of the worst discipline problems you'll experience. I find them harder to teach than Resource and Behavioral Disorder (bad kids) classes, because the classes are MUCH larger, and the potential for vandalism is greater.

A typical day

Let's say you have filled out all the required forms and are eagerly awaiting your first call. What will your day be like? My day starts at 5:30 a.m. with a call from Nadine at the substitute office. This morning, she offers me a choice: Resource at Brockbank Junior High, or English at Cyprus High School.

Resource is supposed to be a small class for students who need academic help, but in most schools it ends up being a catch-all for the students nobody wants, usually because of discipline problems. So I choose English at Cyprus. Nadine tells me the teacher's name, and I'm ready to start my day. I bring with me a briefcase containing some puzzles and games I've collected over the years, for students who finish early. I also bring a red pencil or pen, a couple of regular pens, and two or three #2 lead pencils. I try to time my arrival for 30 minutes before class starts.

At school, I report to the office. The secretary tells me where to find the classroom, the faculty lounge, and the roll sheets, and gives me a folder containing a map of the school, the bell schedule, and other things a substitute is expected to know. For example, if the school has printed discipline referral forms, a few will be in the folder. These days, most schools use computers to take the roll.

Taking roll is probably the most important activity of a sub's day, since school budgets are based on enrollment. Never lend pencils or other "office supplies" to students without security. They break them into bits and fling them at each other. They also make remarkable booby-traps out of staples.

The teacher's lesson plan is usually in her mailbox with the roll sheets, or on her desk. A really efficient teacher will tell you exactly what to do all day long. Elementary school teachers are generally better about this than secondary school teachers. A less efficient one may just say something like, "Show the Shakespeare video in my desk drawer." A really inconsiderate teacher may leave no instructions at all. One reason I like to get to school early is to allow time to contact the teacher (the office will call her for you) if I need more information than she gave me.

The information you receive will also tell you the teacher's daily schedule. It's best to go along with this, even if it would be more convenient to make a few small changes. Children are creatures of habit. It makes them much easier to handle if they know what to expect. Secondary schools divide the day into class periods, and you will have several different classes to teach each day.

Surprise! One or more of those classes may not be what you were expecting. Nadine said this teacher teaches English, and so she does. But she didn't tell Nadine that she also coaches the girls' volleyball team! Rather than risk trying to supervise 20 pubescent girls playing volleyball without blushing, I ask the secretary to arrange a trade with another substitute or even a regular teacher for that hour. Luckily, it doesn't happen until fifth period, so she has time to ask around. Early morning is a school secretary's busiest time of the day. She runs the school, so don't antagonize her with early morning demands.

Another item on your schedule will likely be a "Prep" or "Conference" period. Since you have no preparation to do for your classes, this amounts to a rest period for you—another benefit of teaching secondary school. Elementary teachers don't get prep periods. Instead, the whole school may have a weekly "short day," usually on

Friday. The students go home after lunch, while the teachers stay and prepare for the next week. If you are called to sub on a "short day," you will go home early, but you won't be paid for a full day.

Some high schools are now going to "block" schedules, where each class is two periods long. The students attend only odd numbered class periods one day, even the next. This makes your classes about 90 minutes long, instead of the traditional 45. If you are lucky and the teacher's prep period falls on the day you are subbing you will only work four hours, but will be paid for the full day. Otherwise, you'll have to work the full six hours without a prep period.

Most secondary schools have two or three lunch periods each day, called "A," "B," or "C" lunch. It would be nice if your assigned lunch period were on your schedule, but it probably won't be. If the secretary doesn't tell you—ASK! The only other way to tell is to wait until nobody shows up for class. This can easily cost you five or ten minutes of your 25 minute lunch break. If you buy the school lunch ($1.50 or so), go directly to the head of the cafeteria line. Rank has its privileges. You may be required to buy your ticket before school starts in the morning. Again, asking is the only way to know. If you bring your own lunch, there's a refrigerator in the faculty lounge, as well as snack and pop machines and microwave ovens.

Playing the game

First period of the day is always a bit confused. Often the students are unaware that they will have a substitute until they see you. This is the time to get the drop on them in the age-old game of "Get the Sub." For you, winning means actually teaching somebody something. For the students, it means taking over the class. In a tie, you keep control, but they don't learn much. You get paid regardless—tie goes to the sub!

Pay close attention to the first couple of kids who walk into the classroom. A kid who walks in, greets you politely, and sits down is likely the teacher's pet. You can almost always believe what she tells you.

If a kid walks in, yells, "We got a substitute!" and runs out of the

oom, you've just identified the ringleader of the class, your chief oppo-
nent in the game. His strategy is always the same—be friendly but
show increasing disrespect until he reaches the point of open rudeness.
Before then, however, his buddies will begin to copy him, and the class
will be completely out of your control. You can tell if this is happening
by your own voice. If you have to shout, you are losing. If you are losing, call for help from a nearby teacher. Better to lose face than to lose
control of the class.

The students never realize they are following a well-known pattern,
so it's easy to circumvent their tactics. First, NEVER let the ringleader
or his followers get away with the least bit of disrespect, profanity, etc.
Don't be afraid of appearing mean or prudish. A reputation for meanness is one of the best weapons in your arsenal. You will almost certainly teach one of these kids again someday, and his wail of horror at
seeing you will guarantee an easy class!

Second, never, ever lose your temper. If you do, you have lost the
game. The best subs don't even raise their voices. Some carry a little
bell to ring, or some other attention getting device. I carry a gavel and
a block of wood in my briefcase. But even flicking the lights off and on
works, as long as the students know they have something to lose. I
count the seconds it takes them to get quiet, then add them on to the
class time at the end of the period. If it adds up to two minutes or more,
I let them "work it off" by an equal amount of absolute silence just
before the end of class. But I don't tell them this in advance. Dedicating
the last five minutes of class for clean-up and quiet-down will reduce
your stress a lot.

For individual infractions, the regular teacher usually writes the student's name on the board, with checks after the name for repeat offens-
es. Somewhere in the room will be a schedule of escalating punishments, based on the number of checks. I have found this doesn't work
well for me, as I forget the students' names. Teachers are supposed to
keep a current seating chart available for you, but they seldom do. In

207

elementary schools, it's best to make a name tag for each child's desk at the beginning of class. In secondary schools, the classes are so large and the periods so brief, you can use up half the period this way. Junior high students should NEVER be asked to write their names on anything except graded assignments. Anything else they will take as an opportunity to write fake and/or obscene names. If you start seeing "Ber Dover" and "Anna Rexick," watch out! You are losing control of the class.

I prefer individual punishments that don't require me to know the student's name, such as making a litterbug "play janitor" by picking up all the paper on the floor, or taking him to a nearby teacher for the rest of the hour. (Clear this with the other teacher first!) Regardless of the official discipline policy, I give each kid three "strikes," then send him to the office. Of course, his buddies volunteer to "escort" him there, and you can bet they'll never arrive. I send him alone, but write his departure time on the referral slip and in my notes. I warn him that I'm going to check his arrival time, and I always do. I have NEVER had a student fail to arrive within three minutes. The troublemakers all know the way there! If you send your first period ringleader to the office right away your reputation for meanness will get around, and you'll have an easy day. Some of the kids won't like you, but the good students will.

Tricks of the trade

The regular teacher knows her subject and classes intimately, and nearly always takes longer to cover a lesson than it will take you. So you'll often have time left over. You can allow the kids to study, talk quietly, etc. if you wish. They will be amazed that you turned out nice after all. Better yet, you can bring something for them to do that they will find interesting. I bring my guitar to school. French classes especially like learning "Head, Shoulders, Knees, and Toes" in French, or Christmas carols in season. Sometimes we serenade another class, with advance permission. All classes love to get substitutes talking about themselves, and sometimes I indulge them, but only after the lesson is one. Teens appreciate candor in adults, and enjoy the opportunity to find out what things are really like from someone who's been there. I may decline to answer their questions, but I never, ever lie to them.

As long as they're well-behaved, and are not taking a test, I let students work in groups of three or four. Much of the conversation has little to do with the assignment, but as long as there's actual learning taking place, who cares? I go over the answers at the end of class, anyway. Groups that are rowdy or loud get one warning, then I separate them.

Often, the teacher leaves a video for the kids to watch. They hate them, and so do I. Watching videos requires you to turn the lights off or down, giving the kids a wonderful opportunity to bedevil each other and you without being caught. Some teachers require students to take notes on videos.

In my experience, this seldom helps. The students fill up half a page (or whatever the requirement is) in the first ten minutes, then it's back to playing "Beat the Sub." If you must show a video, write questions about it on the board or pass out a worksheet, and warn them when each answer is coming up. Of course, you can't do this until you've seen it yourself.

If you have special knowledge of the subject, contact the teacher and ask permission to depart from the lesson plan. I've never been turned down. I tell geography students about my travels. I tell science classes about my alternative energy house. I tell English classes what it's like to be a part-time freelance writer. The possibilities are endless. Teachers will love you for bringing to their classes something special they cannot do themselves.

It's polite to leave the teacher a note, telling her how each class went, what material you covered, which students were especially helpful, and which need discipline. If you love a class, leave the teacher your phone number. If a whole class just can't seem to get with the program, I take a notebook around and start writing down the names of students who are on task, without saying why. Eventually, some will ask why they are being "written up," since they aren't doing anything wrong. I just qui etly tell them that I'm making a "good list" for their teacher. Word spreads like wildfire!

It's fun playing these kinds of games with the kids, but it's even more fun when you manage to teach someone something they were having trouble with. And even if you "lose" once in a while and a class gets away from you, you'll still get paid just for trying. It sure beats work ing for a living! 🍂

Other titles available from
Backwoods Home Magazine

The Best of the First Two Years
A Backwoods Home Anthology—The Third Year
A Backwoods Home Anthology—The Fourth Year
A Backwoods Home Anthology—The Fifth Year
A Backwoods Home Anthology—The Sixth Year
A Backwoods Home Anthology—The Seventh Year
A Backwoods Home Anthology—The Eighth Year
A Backwoods Home Anthology—The Ninth Year
A Backwoods Home Anthology—The Tenth Year
A Backwoods Home Anthology—The Eleventh Year
A Backwoods Home Anthology—The Twelfth Year
A Backwoods Home Anthology—The Thirteenth Year
A Backwoods Home Anthology—The Fourteenth Year
Emergency Preparedness and Survival Guide
Backwoods Home Cooking
Can America Be Saved From Stupid People
Chickens—a beginner's handbook
Starting Over—Chronicles of a Self-Reliant Woman
Dairy Goats—a beginner's handbook
Self-reliance—Recession-proof your pantry